RIOT

AT THE CALC EXAM

and Other Mathematically Bent Stories

Colin Adams

RIOT

AT THE
CALC
EXAM

+y

$y=4-x^2$

$y=2x+2$

-2 -1   1   2   +x

and Other Mathematically Bent Stories

AMS

AMERICAN MATHEMATICAL SOCIETY
Providence, Rhode Island

2000 *Mathematics Subject Classification*. Primary 97A90, 00A05, 00A08.

Cover art ©2009 American Mathematical Society.
Interior illustrations ©2009 Colin Adams.
All artwork provided by Pier Gustafson.
Visit his website at http:www.piergustafson.com.

For additional information and updates on this book, visit
www.ams.org/bookpages/mbk-62

Library of Congress Cataloging-in-Publication Data

Adams, Colin Conrad.
    Riot at the calc exam and other mathematically bent stories / Colin Adams.
        p. cm.
    Includes bibliographical references.
    ISBN 978-0-8218-4817-3 (alk. paper)
    1. Mathematics—Humor. I. Title.

QA99.A235   2009
510.2′07—dc22   2009009835

Contents

NOTES

Introduction

Let's try something. I will say a word, and you respond with a word. Ready? Peanut butter.... Did you say jelly? I thought so. Here's another one. Strawberries.... Did you say cream? Pretty amazing huh? It's as if I can read your mind, even though I am not in the room with you. In fact, I am not in the room with you. I am not even in the same time coordinate as you, having written this some time in the past before you read it. As I write this, right now, *I am reading your mind... in the future!* Pretty amazing. Let's try another one. Math.... What did you say? Did you say humor? I am willing to bet that you did. Because everyone associates math with humor.

Why is it that you can't think about math without thinking about humor? Why is it, when you walk down the corridor of a math building at any major university, you hear peals of laughter and snorts of pleasure coming out of the classrooms? Why do so many comedians complete Ph.D.'s in mathematics simply to improve their ability to deliver a punchline? Why, when students receive their graded exams in math classes, do they laugh out loud?

Why? Well, we all know the answer. Because math is fun. There is nothing quite so much fun as math. Certainly not ice cream. Certainly not sex. And certainly not physics.

But it wasn't always that way. Believe it or not, there was a time when math and humor were considered disjoint sets.

No one is sure when math and humor appeared together for the first time. Many attribute it to the time Karl Friedrich Gauss (1777-1855) mistakenly stumbled into a stand-up club in Göttingen, and managed, with just a few infinite series, to bring down the house. Others suggest that it was the early comedy team known as the Bernoulli Brothers. Still others attribute it to the first use of the word "functor". But what we know for sure is that now, when you think of math, you just start chuckling.

Why then, is this the first book of humorous math stories? Why aren't there whole sections of bookstores devoted to this topic? If math and humor go hand-in-hand like a glove and ummm, a hand, then why isn't literature littered with this stuff?

Again, I will read your mind. Right now, you are saying to yourself, that's right. I haven't seen any books of humorous math stories. And given how humorous math is, what could possibly be the explanation for that?

Clearly, there is only one logical conclusion we can draw. The answer is simple. Someone, somehow, and I won't name names, has kept this material from the American public. Yes, they have used the full power of the American government (think FBI, CIA, FDA, ATF, FTD) to hide the fact that math and humor go together like water and wet pants.

Of course, you may be asking yourself, why would these unnamed people in the highest echelons of government want to keep this humorous math literature from a public hungering for it? Why do they want people to believe that math is dreary, dull, quantitative, and logical in the extreme? Why have they wanted to convince us all that mathematics has, as their PR lackeys put it, "a dearth of mirth"?

There is only one logical answer. Because they fear the marriage of math and humor. They fear it the same way some people fear interspecies marriage. Simply because they don't understand it.

So I have written this book, I hope somehow it slips past the government censors and gets out to the public. And I hope the public seizes on it, and buys millions of copies and it soars to the top of the bestseller lists, not because of the buckets of money I would make, but because people need to satisfy their natural desire to see math and humor together.

But I realize this scenario is extremely unlikely, and the entire book is most likely an exercise in futility. For if the censor reads through this book and chuckles once, just once, that will be enough to relegate it to a vault deep in the bowels of Washington, and to keep it out of your reach.

But perhaps, just perhaps, we will get lucky. Perhaps the government censor will not find anything funny in the entire book, and then she or he will let you read it. We can always hope, can't we?

Notes on the Introduction

No particular mathematical background is necessary to read these stories. Although there are some jokes, references, and/or themes that will be understood on first read only by the more mathematically inclined, I have included notes at the end of the book that explain the relevant material. These notes can (and often should) be skipped by those with more mathematical background.

Acknowledgments

First of all, I want to thank Edward Burger, Susan Loepp and Frank Morgan, three of my colleagues at Williams College. I ran drafts of many of these stories by them and received excellent suggestions and helpful critiques. They were generous with their time and gentle with their criticism.

I would also like to thank Tom Garrity, another member of my department with whom I have worked on two humorous math DVDs, "The Great Pi/e Debate", and "The United States of Mathematics Presidential Debate". It is always fun to be in the same room as Tom.

More generally, I am grateful to the entire Mathematics and Statistics Department at Williams College. I am lucky to be a member of what must be one of the most amusing and friendly departments in academics today. We usually eat lunch together in the seminar room, and several of the ideas for the stories in this collection were generated by random remarks and/or discussions over lunch. Ask someone in the department how you prevent anyone from sitting in the seat next to you on a Southwest flight. You will get a sense of the level of discourse.

I would also like to thank my editors at the *Mathematical Intelligencer*, Chandler Davis and Marjorie Senechal. They have been extremely supportive of my writing for a long time, and I greatly appreciate their editorial suggestions and considered opinions.

A special thanks goes to Ina Mette. When she was the mathematics editor at Springer Verlag and I first suggested a book of stories, it was her idea that the stories would make a good column for the Mathematical Intelligencer. Over the years, I have benefited greatly from her advice and friendship. Ina is now a mathematics editor at the American Mathematical Society. In producing this book, I have also worked with her colleague Edward Dunne, who has been very helpful and supportive of this project and others.

The illustrations for the book were created by Pier Gustafson. In addition to having excellent artistic sense, Pier adds clever twists that inevitably enhance all his work. Stop by www.piergustafson.com to see more.

One of the stories, "Math Talk" was co-authored with Lew Ludwig. I thank him for the enjoyment I derived from working on it with him and his permission to include it here.

Some of these stories have been performed as skits at colleges and math conferences, including *Mangum P.I., A Difficult Delivery, Trial and Error, The Mathematical Ethicist, Math Talk, Research Announcement, Math Fall Fashion Preview, A Killer Theorem, Vital Signs,* and *Rumpled Stiltsken.* Numerous performers have participated in those presentations, and did a wonderful job. I thank them all. For any of the above-listed stories that do not appear here in script form, please feel free to request script versions from me if you would like to perform them.

All of the stories in this volume first appeared in the column, *Mathematically Bent,* in the *Mathematical Intelligencer,* with a few exceptions. *Pythagoras's Darkest Hour* first appeared in Math Horizons. *Vital Sines* has not appeared before this volume. *The Integral: A Horror Story* was rightfully deemed too violent for the Mathematical Intelligencer and is also appearing here for the first time. But I think you can take it.

The S.S. Riemann

The S.S. Riemann embarked on its maiden voyage from the dock of the Department of Mathematics, Yale University, on April 2, 2009. Weighing in at 934 pages, and including a separate 200,000-line computer proof of the main lemma, she was the most massive theorem ever produced up to that time. There wasn't another theorem afloat on the mathematical ocean that compared.

She had a crew of over 31, including Captain Alphonse Huber, a full professor and Fields medalist, five other full professors, eleven associate professors, eight assistant professors, and six post docs in steerage. Various grad students tagged along for the ride.

Yes, she was the crown jewel in the fleet of theorems that had come out of Yale. Designed to survive any catastrophe, she was built with expendable lemmas shielding her bow. There were back-up lemmas and back-up lemmas to those. The proof was constructed with a graph-like structure so that if an edge were to be destroyed, there would be another path to the same point in the proof. Mathematicians marveled at the intricacy of her design. The computer proof used interval arithmetic, making it as rigorous as if it had all been done by hand. They said she was unsinkable.

This first cruise was a shake-down run, to get the kinks out; just a quick trip to MIT and Harvard for a going-over by the experts there, and then on to the University of Michigan for a week-long seminar.

The subsequent voyage would be a straight shot to the *Annals of Mathematics.*

As she departed from the wharf in New Haven, the graduate students cried out and waved exultantly, throwing streamers. Bands played exuberant marches. Administrators made promises that they knew they couldn't keep. It was a sight to behold.

Once in Cambridge, they put her through her paces. The crew cranked up the logical engines, and she forged ahead. Nothing could slow her down. She sliced through questions like a scull in the Charles River. The crew oiled a proposition here, tightened a corollary there, and she lived up to her reputation as the most powerful theorem on the mathematical sea.

At Harvard, her reception was grand. Wine and imported cheese on sesame crackers, and little spanikopita hors d'oeuvres. No expense was spared. The crew reveled in the attention. After a colloquium replete with standing ovation, they turned her and headed for Michigan.

Ann Arbor was cool at that time of year, but no one was overly concerned. After all, she was the queen of the ocean. They docked amid much fanfare. But the hubbub died down quickly, and a week-long set of lectures in the analysis seminar began.

It started out fine. Huber remained at the helm at first. But soon he relaxed. She had proved herself in Cambridge. He could ease off and let other members of the crew pilot the craft. As the week wore on, the seminar shrank in size, and they were down to a handful of experts.

Late in the week, many of the crew had dozed off, and others had wandered out for coffee. It was a post doc, Dimmick, who was on watch when he realized there was something off the port bow, something in a question asked by the diminutive Professor Feisberg, an expert in holomorphic functions. At first, Dimmick wasn't sure that it would amount to anything, so he did not sound the alarm. But as the issue loomed larger in the darkening seminar room, he realized how serious it was.

"Counterexample, counterexample, dead ahead," he screamed out. "Full reverse, full reverse. All hands on deck." The professors leapt to their feet. Everyone grabbed for chalk and erasers. But the theorem ground on toward the immovable object ahead. Nothing could stop their forward momentum in time. The counterexample loomed out of the darkness, tall, white, stark against the evening sky. Some of the graduate students remained oblivious to the impending disaster, as they played intramural soccer on an adjacent field.

Professor Huber tried to convince the crew that it would be all right. "She can withstand it," he said. But crew members were leaping out the door of the seminar room at an alarming rate.

When the collision occurred, it seemed to happen in slow motion.

There was a grinding crunch. Lemmas sloughed off the prow. Edges of the graph-like structure buckled under the impact. The hull seemed to crumple up like the ego of a jobless Ph.D.

Almost immediately, they realized she was going to go down.

Huber turned to the communications officer. "Reynolds," he said. "Use your cell phone to call the nearest functional analyst. I think it's Alder at Wisconsin. We are going to need help once we are in the water. There aren't enough hypotheses to go around."

As Reynolds dialed frantically, the Captain tried to quell the growing panic.

"Everyone, I ask you to remain calm. We have radioed for help."

But Reynolds turned to the Captain with tears running down his cheeks.

"Captain, Captain," he cried. "Alder is in Germany. The nearest functional analyst is in Utah, and there's no way she could get here in time. We're on our own."

There was pandemonium at the doorway to the seminar room, as the mob fought to get out in time.

"Please," shouted the captain. "Let the grad students and post docs have the hypotheses. Show some courage." But full professors were grabbing lemmas and claims as they pushed post docs to the floor in their frantic haste to escape. Reynolds seized a corollary but Huber stopped him. "Reynolds, that won't float."

Dimmick turned to the Captain.

"Sir, we should get out before it's too late."

"I'm not getting out," replied the Captain gravely.

"I'm going down with her."

"I'll go down with her, too, Sir," said Dimmick, trying not to look frightened.

"No," said Huber. "You have your whole career in front of you. Don't throw it away on this ship, as beautiful as she is. Abandon her. You will survive to crew another theorem."

Dimmick shook his head "no" but Huber placed a firm hand on his shoulder.

"That's an order," he said. Dimmick saluted one last time and then scrambled out of the seminar room.

As the afternoon light dimmed, Huber and the crew members who hadn't managed to escape, slowly disappeared beneath the waves, lost forever in the immeasurable ocean known as mathematics.

Some day a ship will leave port again, a ship with the name S.S. Riemann. And that ship will be truly indestructible. And mathematicians around the world will rejoice. But until then, remember to book your passage carefully, and bring along plenty of hypotheses.

Pythagoras's
Darkest Hour

"What the Hades is the matter with you?" asked Triangulus, as he leaned over Pythagoras, whose face was buried in the wine-soaked sleeve of his toga, atop the stone bar. Pythagoras lifted his head groggily.

"What do you want? Leave me alone."

"Oh please, Pythagoras, it doesn't do you any good to drown your sorrows. You are taking this whole thing much too hard." Pythagoras waved him away.

"Hemlock, bartender. Bring me a glass of hemlock."

"Don't be so melodramatic. It's just one theorem."

"Oh, right. Just one theorem. I have been humiliated in front of the entirety of Greek civilization. I have been made a fool. My name will go down in history. They will call it the "Pythagorean Folly". Hold it up to young children as an example of pure stupidity."

"You are exaggerating. In a week, no one will even remember."

"Right! Like they don't remember the Trojan Horse. Like they forgot Oedipus and his tiny mistake. I think you have a slightly warped view of Greek forbearance. Some poet will write an epic

entitled the Pythagoriad, all about what a goat-brain I am. It'll rise
to the top ten and stay there forever."

Pythagoras began to suck on his wine-soaked sleeve.

"Hey, stop that. Remember who you are. You're the leader of
the Pythagorean School of Mathematics."

"Yeah, right. The enrollments have been dropping like the Athe-
nians in the Persian Wars. In another two days, the Pythagorean
School of Mathematics will have an enrollment of one, and that's because you're my slave. Zeus damn it all, I don't have a hope in Hades
of getting out of this.

What made me think I was a mathematician? Huh? I could
have been perfectly happy doing something with my hands. A farmer
maybe. Or a sandal maker. I always thought I had a good eye for
fashion sandals. But no, I had to be a mathematician."

"Pythagoras, I think it was a good idea. $x^2 + y^2 = z^2$. It has a
ring to it."

"Yes, it does, but unfortunately, it isn't true."

"Well, no, I guess not. What made you think that the radius,
circumference, and area of a circle would be related like that?"

"Oh, I don't know. It's just such a pretty equation, that's all.
You can always hope."

"Yes but you probably should have checked at least one example
before announcing the theorem to the Assembly."

"Well, that's apparent now. But give me a break. We're living
during the birth of mathematics here. Some of these things aren't so
obvious."

"Well, maybe there's some way to save it."

"Yeah right."

"What if you kept the equation but tried it on some other object?"

"What do you mean? Like a pyramid? The Egyptians are smart.
Don't you think that if it applied to a pyramid, they would have
noticed by now?"

"True, true, but what about something simpler?"

"Like what?"

"Oh, I don't know. What about a square or a rectangle?"

"Nah, Triangulus, that's no good. There are only two side lengths and all the angles are identical right angles. And the area is just the product of the two side lengths. Nothing works there."

"Well, I guess you need something with three related quantities, maybe all lengths."

"You mean like a comb, with three teeth? No, the teeth would all have the same length. How about a family, with a mother and father and child? We could compare their heights."

"Seems an unlikely relation to hold, Pythagoras, at least for most families. How about we stick to more geometric objects, like a triangle?"

"Oh, I see where you are going. Make x, y, and z the angles of a triangle. Not bad, not bad. Not true, but not bad."

"Actually, I was thinking more the side lengths."

"Yeah, right, Triangulus, like that could work. It's not even true for an equilateral triangle."

"Hmmm, well, maybe we're just not coming at it from the right angle."

"Yeah, the right angle. That's what we need all right." Pythagoras began to suck on his sleeve again. Triangulus tugged it out of his mouth.

"Pythagoras, what about this? What numbers satisfy your equation?"

"Well, there's 3, 4, and 5. $3^2 + 4^2 = 5^2$."

"Can't you make a triangle with sides 3, 4, and 5?"

"Sure, there's a well-known triangle, actually a right triangle with side lengths 3, 4, and 5."

"Well, there."

"In fact, any constant multiple of 3, 4, and 5 satisfies the same equation, and that corresponds to scaling the triangle up or down."

"Okay."

"And 5, 12, and 13. They satisfy the equation. And there is a triangle with side lengths 5, 12, and 13! A right triangle!"

"There you go!"

"Triangulus. You are a genius. I think this is a theorem! After all, it works for at least two examples and all their multiples. Given a right triangle, with sides x, y, and z, where z is the hypotenuse, then $x^2 + y^2 = z^2$. That's it. I'm not sure how to prove it, but with some thought, we can figure that out later. Let's go announce it to the Assembly. My school is saved. My reputation is saved! And this theorem will go down in history as the Pythagoras Triangulus Theorem. And I will make you a free man."

"Oh, Pythagoras, that would be wonderful."

"Yes, yes, of course... but on second thought, I don't know if the Pythagoras Triangulus Theorem is such a good name. It's a bit on the long side."

"Oh... okay."

"And if I free you, then who would there be to pick up the togas at the laundry? And peel the grapes I eat? And figure out the bills? You know how terrible I am with arithmetic. Actually, Triangulus, I'm afraid I can't free you after all."

"I understand, Pythagoras."

"Now let's see. Getting back to my $x^2 + y^2 = z^2$ formula, it says that when x and y are both 1, z^2 must be 2. So an isosceles right triangle with legs of length 1 would have a hypotenuse whose square is 2. I've never seen a number whose square is 2, but since all quantities can be expressed as a fraction of integers, the numerator and denominator of this quantity must be pretty easy to find. I'll tell the Assembly that I have found a truly marvelous fraction whose square is 2, and challenge them to find it!"

"But are you sure such a fraction exists, Pythagoras?"

"Don't be irrational, Triangulus! Of course it does."

"Okay, but perhaps we should try to find it before we challenge others to do so."

"Why don't you work on that Triangulus, and in the mean time, I will try to find integers that satisfy the next equation $x^3 + y^3 = z^3$. That can't be much harder. And hey, if we just increase the exponent, this should be enough to keep us busy for the next two and a half millennia."

"I am sure it will, Pythagoras. I am sure it will."

Mangum, P.I.

The name's Mangum. Dirk Mangum, P.I. Yeah, that's right. I am a Principal Investigator. On a National Science Foundation grant. Didn't start out that way, though. You don't just decide to be a PI. No, you have to earn the right. For me, it wasn't anything I expected. Just a fortuitous set of circumstances, although it didn't seem fortuitous at the time. Quite the contrary.

I was working as a snotnosed postdoc out of a sleazy hole-in-the-wall office in LA. Actually, UCLA to be specific. It was my third year of a three-year appointment, and I didn't have anything to show for the first two years except for a stuffed wastebasket, a pile of empty Orangina bottles and a whole lot of self-doubt.

My story begins on one of those days you get in LA. The sun was shining, a slight breeze was ruffling the palm trees, and it was an even 70 degrees. Actually, I just described every day in LA. It's enough to make you want to scream. Just give me a cloud, or some fog. Or God forbid, a hailstorm. But no, there is the sun, day in day out, beating a drum beat on your brain, banging out it's sunny sun dance until you want to do things that would get you into serious trouble with accounts payable.

I was hunkered down in my office, feet up on the desk, sucking on my second bottle of Orangina for the day. I had been wrestling with the proof of a lemma all afternoon, but it had me in a double overhook headlock and the chances of me ending up anywhere other than flat on the mat were slim indeed. The constant drone of the air conditioner sounded like a UPS truck tackling the continental divide. There was a knock at my door.

"I'm not in," I yelled.

There was a pause and then a second knock. I sighed, lifting my feet off the desk.

"If you won't go away, you might as well come in."

The door swung open and I just about swallowed my bottle of Orangina. Standing in the door was none other than Walter P. Parsnip, chair of the Berkeley Math Department. He was dressed suggestively, in a white button down, top button undone to expose his clavicle, and slacks so worn you could almost see through them at the knee. His shirt clung to his chest, the outline of his bulging stomach obvious for all to see.

I found it hard to believe he was here before me. I used to drool over this guy's articles when I was an undergraduate. He had a career built like a brick shipyard. And talk about legs. He published his first article in 1932, and he was still going strong. Half the functions in Wang Doodle theory were named after Parsnip and the other half were named after his dog.

I gave him a long look up and down and then said as smoothly as I could, "Well come on in here and take a load off."

He took his time coming in, giving my eyeballs a chance to run over his body at will. I took full advantage of the opportunity. He slid into the overstuffed leather chair that sat in front of my desk and stretched his legs out before him.

I noticed a single bead of sweat work its tortuous way down his nose and then drop off, only to land on his extruding lower lip. I gulped.

"I'm...," he started to say.

"Oh, I know who you are," I said, cutting him off. "What I don't know is what someone as hot as you wants with someone as cold as me."

"I'm in trouble," he said.

"Who isn't?" I retorted.

"I'm in deep trouble," he said. He fixed me with a look that would have made me swallow my tongue if I hadn't happened to have been chewing on it at the time.

He leaned forward conspiratorially, giving me a nice view down the inside of his well-used pocket protector. "I've got a theorem. It's a big one."

"I bet it is," I said, trying to sound casual.

But I knew that if Parsnip thought it was big, it would make Riemann Roch look like Zorn's Lemma.

"It implies Canooby."

The Canooby Conjecture, perhaps the biggest open problem in all of Pinched Rumanian Monofield Theory. You solve Canooby, and they deliver the presidency of the American Mathematical Society to your doorstep.

"Doesn't sound like a problem to me," I said.

"It's joint work with Kazdan."

I lifted an eyebrow. Kazdan was the current darling of the math community. Twenty-six years old, Belgian and brilliant. So hot that if he was a waffle iron, you could pour batter in the front end, and get fully cooked waffles out the back. Belgian waffles.

I watched as Parsnip crossed his legs, his pant cuff riding up enough to expose some hairy leg over the top of his black sheer socks. He caught me taking a gander.

"So, what's the problem with working with Kazdan?" I asked.

"Kazdan isn't working with me any more. He dumped me for Vishy."

Shwase Vichy. Youngest faculty member to ever get tenure at Chicago. He was still packing a lunch box. Must have been hard on Parsnip.

"How can I help?" I asked, looking deep into his milky brown eyes. They were eyes you could spend a lot of time looking into. Why you would want to do that, I don't know, but people pick strange hobbies.

"It is a lemma," he said. "Just one lemma I need. With the lemma, I will have my proof."

"What makes you think I can help you with your lemma?" I asked, leaning back in my chair, trying to appear disinterested.

"They tell me you are the best when it comes to the theory of semiupperpseudohypermultitudinal fluxions."

"Well, that was the title of my Ph.D. thesis. But you're the first person to ever pronounce it correctly."

"It is exactly what is needed to solve my dilemma. What will it take to get you to help me, Dirk?"

He placed his hand on mine. I felt the warmth of those gnarled hairy knuckles.

I smiled my most captivating smile. "Who in their right mind would turn down a chance to publish with you?"

He smiled back.

Over the next eight months I devoted myself to the problem. I should have been publishing papers based on my thesis, to ensure a follow-up job, but instead, I thought of nothing but the lemma. I worked on it in the shower. I worked on it in the tub. I even worked on it at the office. It became an obsession.

I started to dream about it. There was one where Parsnip and I were dancing the rhumba and Shwase Vichy danced over, laughed in that falsetto laugh of his and said, "Oh, no, you are not doing math here." I woke up in a cold sweat.

And still, the lemma wouldn't budge. Parsnip notwithstanding, I was ready to give up. It seemed hopeless. But then, one day, as I was stepping off the bus, it hit me. An epiphany. I realized what I had been missing. I couldn't believe my stupidity. When all this time, I had been working on semiupperpseudohypermultitudinal fluxions I should have been thinking about multihyperpseudouppersemitudinal

fluxions. I had been looking at it exactly backward. With this realization, I knew that I had not only solved the problem, but I had
created a whole new field of mathematics.

The other passengers waiting to get off the bus began to push,
but I didn't care. I knew I was right.

I rushed to my office, overwhelmed with excitement. I would have
Parsnip's undying gratitude. A tenured position at Berkeley might
be in the offing. Parsnip picked up his phone on the first ring.

"Hello, Parsnip? I solved your problem."

"You solved it?" he shouted back into the phone. "This is amazing."

"Yes, it is," I said. "Why don't you come on down from Berkeley,
and I'll show it to you. Then you can tell me how great I am."

"No, I can't wait," he said. "Please fax it to me now. I'll come
down Monday."

I should have smelled a double dealing rat, but they have yet to
perfect an odor-producing phone. So I faxed it to him.

The next morning, when I opened the LA Times, I saw the huge
bold headline splashed across the page. "PARSNIP AND KAZDAN
SOLVE CANOOBY". I did swallow my tongue this time, but luckily
I coughed it back up. There was a huge picture of the two of them
shaking hands with the governor. I had been played for a fool.

Figuring out what had happened took me less time than it takes
a barn fly to find sustenance. Parsnip and Kazdan were working on
Canooby the entire time, but they got stuck. They needed help, but
they weren't about to let a pissant postdoc like me get my name on
a theorem as big as this. So they came up with their ruse. Parsnip
comes to see me, acting the jilted collaborator, desperate for my aid.
Sucker that I am, I fall head over heels. They figure I can't resist his
charms, and they're right.

Once they have the fax, I'm history. Nobody will believe a postdoc without a single publication to his name, and with a job disappearing faster than the woolly mammoth. In a year, I would be
pumping Slurpees at the local Seven Eleven.

The first three days, I sat in my office and cried into my Orangina. Although diluted, the salt in the tears added zest. The next three days, I tried to figure out how to franchise salted Orangina.

On the seventh day, I received a grant proposal to review from the National Science Foundation. And wonder of wonders, it was from Kazdan and Parsnip. They wanted five million dollars to study multihyperpseudouppersemitudinal fluxions. Now, why the National Science Foundation sent the proposal to me for review, I'll never know. They certainly didn't know I invented the field. And it's unlikely they realized there was a connection between multihyperpseudouppersemitudinal fluxions and semiupperpseudohypermultitudinal fluxions. But for whatever reason, the osprey of opportunity had come to roost in my lap, and I have to tell you, it felt good having it there.

For the next two weeks, I worked on multihyperpseudouppersemitudinal fluxions. I saw vistas never before glimpsed by man or beast. I wandered the high plateaus of human thought, breathing the rarefied air. To protect myself from the elements, I built little Quonset lemmas, small rounded pup tents, only made out of words and symbols. I thought I might need them if it rained. And it did rain. First a little bit. And then a lot. It poured as if the high plateau of human thought was a giant toilet bowl and somebody, I don't know who, as this analogy is confusing me a bit, somebody flushed that toilet. There was a deluge. For you see, I realized that multihyperpseudouppersemitudinal fluxions have absolutely nothing to do with pinched Rumanian monofields or the Canooby Conjecture. Yes, I had been mistaken. Oops. My bad.

So I wrote a one-hundred page review of the grant proposal, pointing out the error, and explaining how the field of multihyperpseudouppersemitudinal fluxions, although useless for the purpose outlined in the proposal, was in fact, just what is needed to model appropriate salt content in carbonated beverages.

Then I drove up to Berkeley, arriving at the height of a lecture being given by Parsnip on Canooby. Although he saw me enter the lecture hall, it didn't seem to shake him in the least. No, he seemed to relish the opportunity to show me how carefully he had constructed his deception. I sat down in the front, right next to Kazdan.

Parsnip was going on about functor this and functor that, when I raised my hand. He paused. I stood up and said, "Cut to the chase. Who invented multihyperpseudouppersemitudinal fluxions?"

He actually smiled. "As everyone knows, it was Kazdan and I. Don't you read the papers?"

"Oh, yes, I read the papers," I said. "But you know what they say. Don't believe everything you read."

"Young man, I'm not sure I understand what you are getting at. Should I know you? Are you a graduate student visiting from out of town? Perhaps you are looking for the cookies. They are in the Math Lounge."

"The name's Mangum, Dirk Mangum," I said calmly. "But you know that."

There must have been something in the way I said my name that made him uncomfortable. The self-assured smile fell from his face for just a second. Then I fired. "If multihyperpseudouppersemitudinal fluxions play such an important role in the solution of the Canooby Conjecture, then why is it that they aren't connected? Canooby assumes that the fluxions are connected."

Parsnip's expression went from unsure to shocked in a split second. I had clearly hit my mark. He gripped the lectern to support himself as the blood fled from his face. He was clearly in pain.

"What do you mean they aren't connected?" he croaked.

Kazdan leaped up from his chair, but there was nothing he could do. The audience sat in stunned silence as they watched the tableau unfold. I fired again.

"I mean they aren't connected. Not attached to one another. Capice? There is space in between them. Here's one and here's another and you can't get from the one to the other. Comprende? THEY COME IN MORE THAN ONE PIECE. So they don't apply to Canooby!"

Parsnip fell to one knee. A shudder went through the audience. Kazdan grabbed my sleeve, for what purpose I don't know, but I shrugged him off, and he fell back into his chair, stricken.

I smiled then at Parsnip. He reached up a trembling hand in my direction. "Dirk," he said, "help me, Dirk."

For a moment, I almost felt sorry for him. But I got over it.

"See you around," I said. "Actually, I kind of doubt I will." I walked out the door as he crumpled to the floor.

When I got back to LA, I submitted the grant review. To quote from the letter I received:

"Never before have we received a review that so clearly demonstrates the genius of the reviewer, while also demonstrating the entire paucity of ideas in the original proposal. Not only do we reject the proposal, but we would like to give you a grant. How does a million dollars sound? And that's just for the first year. Any time you want additional funds, day or night, just call the director of NSF. Her home phone number appears at the bottom."

Parsnip and Kazdan were so embarrassed that they dropped out of Pinched Rumanian Monofield theory entirely. Now they work in probability, mostly taking turns pulling colored golf balls out of bins. I ended up staying at UCLA. After a while, you get used to the weather. And I have been a PI ever since. If you need a PI, give me a call. My number's in the book.

Overcoming Math Anxiety

There is a crippling disease that has a vice grip on the nation. It is lowering the Gross National Product, causing whole communities to break out in hives and convincing many people to stay home with the covers over their heads. Of course, I could only be talking about Math Anxiety.

This poison ivy of the soul has a long and mangy history. Isaac Newton himself had such a bad case that while he wrote the *Principia Mathematica* he was shaking from head to foot. Joseph Louis Lagrange was bedridden for a week before he could bring himself to write down his famous multiplier. And Evariste Galois preferred risking his life in a duel to grappling with the mathematics that made him so nauseous.

Of course, math anxiety is not the only ailment associated with mathematics. There is math incontinence, math male pattern baldness, math itch, and runny math nose. However, today, we will focus our attention on math anxiety, leaving those other maladies to a series of articles that I am writing for the *Notices of the American Mathematical Society*.

How do you know if you suffer from math anxiety? Here is a quick test. Check off each of the symptoms that you experience when confronted with mathematics.

Symptoms of math anxiety:

   A. Hyperventilation.

   B. Holding your breath.

   C. Sweating profusely, while holding your breath.

   D. Sweating profusely, while holding Spanier's "Algebraic Topology".

   E. Eating other people's bag lunches.

   F. Uncontrollable shaking, hopping, or doing the rhumba.

   G. Wearing a heavy winter coat in the Math Resource Room.

   H. Putting pencils in your nostrils or ear holes.

   I. Sucking your thumb.

   J. Sucking your T.A.'s thumb.

   K. Rapid heart beat.

   L. Rapid pulse.

   M. Rapid heart beat but no pulse.

   N. Rapid pulse, but no heart beat.

   O. No pulse or heart beat.

   P. K, L, but not O.

   Q. P, M, N, but not L.

   R. Not R.

   S. Extreme nausea, accompanied by hallucinations of large mammals lecturing you on Euclid's parallel postulate.

   T. The feeling that you and calculus are in a custody battle over your mathematical future and the judge has ordered you to make child-support payments.

   U. The sensation that someone has poured soda water up your nose, and now expects you to thank them for doing so.

V. Dizziness, accompanied by an inability to stand straight on an inclined plane.

W. The feeling that the alphabet is endless.

X. A thousand red ants are crawling over your body, biting and stinging you until you want to scream.

Y. The impression that a thousand red ants are crawling over your body, biting and stinging you until you want to scream.

Z. The feeling that you are running out of ideas, but you must complete a list.

For each of the symptoms that you checked off, write down the number 6.9986. Add these numbers together. Divide by 2π. Take the natural log of the result. Add 1.145, and subtract 1.946. Exponentiate the result. If you are now sweating profusely and feel like you ate bad tuna, you have math anxiety.

(Note: Or you may have eaten bad tuna. If so, you may be suffering from gastronomic masochism. I should have an article out on that in about a week. Try to hang on until then.)

Many presidents suffered from math anxiety, including all of the presidents from 1872-1891 and Teddy Roosevelt, who had to wear diapers as he charged up San Juan Hill, knowing he would need to count the enemy once he got to the top. Sharon Stone breaks into a torrential sweat when asked to give a proof of the central limit theorem, as does Woody Harrelson. Ed Begley, Jr. refuses to appear in any movie involving a covariant functor.

Psychologists have settled on the following four treatments for math anxiety:

1. B.F. Skinner Approach: Here, the student is hooked up to an anxiety detector (usually a rabbit taped to the student's leg). A trigonometry lecture begins. As soon as the rabbit senses anxiety on the part of the student, it rings a bell. The student is immediately forced to run a maze, at the end of which he or she is force-fed a pellet of rat food.

2. The Nurturing Approach: The professor begins the lecture, and as soon as he sees a student looking uncomfortable, he stops the

lecture, comes over and gives the student a warm hug. And he says, "Don't worry, you can do it. You're special. We're all special. Love is all around, if you just let it in." The other students in the auditorium come over, take hands, form a giant circle around the student and sway back and forth, singing songs about how great Coke tastes.

3. Confronting Your Fear Approach: The student is tied to the chair. A drill sargeant screams in their face, "You want to know about real anxiety? You have no idea! I'm going to show you real anxiety. I'm going to make you wish you could hide your head in a big fat textbook and never come out again."

4. Nature's Own Approach: The student is tied to a large rock and thrown in a pond. If the student floats to the surface, the rock is replaced by a larger rock and the process is repeated. If the student does not float to the surface, he or she is declared cured.

Although much has been learned, there are still many important questions to pursue.

Will there ever be a vaccine for math anxiety? And if so, will it be one of those ones where you swallow a pink cube of sugar? Should triskadekophobia be considered a type of math anxiety? Are math anxiety and math phobia the same or just slightly different? These are just a few of the issues addressed in my upcoming anthology, published by the *Journal of the Mathematical Psychoses Institute*.

Until this scourge can be cured, we will need dedicated facilities: ambulances to rush those with sudden-onset math anxiety to emergency rooms staffed by ready Ph.D. math educators, quarantine wings in hospitals to prevent ebola-like epidemics. And most importantly, we will need substantial federal grants to support those of us who are at the cutting edge of research in this seminal field. Some day perhaps, no one will tremble at the sight of a percentage sign. Lunches will not be lost to logarithms. And researchers like me will need to find other sources of support. But in the meantime, continue to read my papers on the subject.

A Difficult Delivery

"Oh, my god, it hurts."

"It's okay, honey. You're almost there."

"It's splitting me wide open!"

"You can do it, honey," said Jeff.

"What did I do to deserve this?" screamed Karen.

They had met in the Math Lounge while grad students. Although Karen was an algebraic geometer and Jeff was a number theorist, it didn't seem to matter. Their love transcended the bounds of their respective mathematical specializations. But little was expected of the union. Dr. Sylvia Vittle, Karen's advisor, had urged her to reconsider. In her Austrian accent, she said, "There are lots of strong algebraic geometers out there. Look at Brogan from UCLA. Or Stigglemeyer from Brown. Why settle for a number theorist?" But Karen knew her heart and the two were married three weeks after they both received their Ph.D.'s.

One morning, four months into the marriage, as they sat at the kitchen table sipping their morning coffee, Karen cleared her throat. Jeff looked up from his morning paper, "Zero-Free Regions for Dirichlet L-Functions".

"Um, Jeff, there's something I want to tell you."

"Yes, honey, what is it?"

"Remember that night two months ago when we stayed up until 3:00 in the morning talking about jet bundles?"

He smiled provocatively. "Who could forget it?"

"Well, about three weeks later, I found myself having trouble sleeping at night."

"Yes?"

"I just couldn't seem to get some of the ideas out of my head. I was waking up in the morning feeling lousy."

"Uh huh."

"So, I guess what I am trying to say is that I think I may be with theorem."

"Oh my God," gasped Jeff as he reached for her hand across the table. "Really? You think so? How can we find out for sure?"

"Well, I have a test that Dr. Vittle gave me. Just a set of possible counterexamples. We can see if it withstands them."

"Okay, definitely, let's do it. Should I do anything?"

"No, just wait here. I can do it in the study. It shouldn't take more than a half hour."

Karen pulled the belt of her bathrobe tight, picked up a pencil and a pad of paper and marched off to the study. After waiting impatiently for 20 minutes, Jeff knocked on the door. "Karen, are you doing okay?"

"Just a few more counterexamples to try, honey. Shouldn't take much longer."

Fifteen minutes later, Karen threw open the door. Jeff leapt up from the kitchen table.

"So?"

She threw her arms around him. "It's true. I am with theorem."

"Yahoo!" said Jeff. "We're going to be published!"

The next day, they made an appointment with Dr. Vittle.

"Well, yes it is unusual, but it is not unheard of. Look at the Atiyah-Singer Index Theorem. That was a product of a topologist and an analyst. But these matches are risky. I want to put you on a strict regimen of ten pages of algebraic number theory a day, say, Cohen's book.

"And when it is time for the theorem to come, it is important to be ready. Have you considered taking a Lemmas class? They are good preparation mentally and physically for the big event."

Karen woke in the middle of the night in a cold sweat. Calculations raced through her head. It appeared that the kernel of the Sowklitz operator was, in fact, a left R-module. She grabbed Jeff's arm.

"Jeff, Jeff, wake up. I think it's here!"

Jeff leapt out of bed, already dressed. "Okay, look. Stay calm. I'll call Dr. Vittle. We can meet her down at the university. You get dressed."

Karen stopped by the side of the bed. "Oh goodness, that was a big idea. It's coming fast. We need to hurry."

They arrived at the university and raced up to the faculty lounge. Dr. Vittle was waiting for them there with several clean pads of paper. "Here," she said to Karen, "you sit here." She turned to Jeff. "Are you going to be here through the whole process?"

"It's as much my theorem as hers," he said.

"Just like a number theorist," laughed Vittle. "You make one small contribution nine months ago, and you think you have done all the work."

"Hey, that contribution nine months ago was key. Without it there would be no theorem."

"Yes, but I don't see you in much pain right now."

"You don't like me very much, do you?"

"Don't take it personally. I don't like any number theorists. I am going to go down to my office, but I will check on you in a bit."

"What's her problem with number theorists?" asked Jeff as soon as Vittle had disappeared down the stairs.

"Don't you know? She was collaborating with Smythe, and one day he saw a talk on wavelets, the hot new thing. Dumped Dr. Vittle like a sack of old conjectures. She swore she would never get involved with another number theorist for as long as she lived."

Karen sat at the table. Jeff paced back and forth. Every once in a while she would say, "Ah, um, I think, maybe, ..., maybe..., oh, no not yet." Then suddenly, she screamed, "John, this is it. Quick, get Dr. Vittle." Symbols spilled out on the page. It was agonizing and amazing at the same time. John flew down the stairs three at a time, and returned almost immediately with Dr. Vittle. Karen was writing furiously.

Vittle peered over Karen's shoulder. "Ah, yes, things are going well. Looks like a big one."

Karen tore page after page off the pad. Vittle turned to John and pointed at one of the sheets of paper. "If you don't think it would be too difficult for you, perhaps you could clean up that lemma there."

John sat down and slowly began to write. Karen was scribbling like mad, as sweat dripped off her brow. She was breathing heavy. Suddenly she tensed. "Oh, my God," she screamed. "It's huge."

"It's okay," coached Dr. Vittle. "Relax and just let it come out."

Karen tore filled sheets off the pad, one after another. She sketched diagrams and figures. Equations with subindices on superindices flowed from her pen. Then her eyes opened wide. "I see it," she gasped. "I see it all." She furiously wrote another half page worth of equations, stopped suddenly and then, awestruck, wrote "QED" at the bottom of the page. There was a moment of complete silence and then she collapsed on the table.

"Are you all right?" John gasped, grasping her by the shoulders.

"Of course she is all right," said Vittle. "Let her rest. She has just given birth."

Karen raised her head slowly from the table, a beatific smile on her lips. "Where is it? Can I hold my theorem?"

"Of course you can," said Vittle. She scooped up the pages, pulling one from John's grasp, and laid the pile in Karen's arms.

Karen cradled the pages carefully. "It's really beautiful isn't it?" she said.

Vittle nodded. "It's a healthy theorem, probably nine to ten pages in 12-point type. What will you name it?"

Karen looked at John tentatively. "Well, we were thinking of calling it the Bounded Co-Generation Theorem, but after what we have just been through, I was thinking maybe the Constrained Optimization Theorem."

John smiled. "I think that's a wonderful name, honey."

"Well, I would like to keep an eye on it tonight. Make sure it's robust enough to stand up to the referees," said Vittle. "And then in the morning, we will send it to the *Annals of Mathematics*."

"The *Annals*?" John gasped. "Even in my wildest dreams, I didn't imagine.... Oh, Karen, I love you."

The two hugged each other, cradling the theorem between them, and even Dr. Vittle smiled.

A Proof of God

It was one of those Wednesday afternoons when Monday seems a distant memory and Saturday has shrunk to an unreachable pinprick in the future. I had just finished teaching my seminar on Boolean Algebras and was settling down in my office with a much-needed cup of coffee. Having just placed my feet up on the desk, I was startled by a knock at the door. Oh no, I thought to myself, it's probably Bunsen. Bunsen was one the weakest students to have ever graced a campus, and there was nothing more disheartening than the appearance of his hangdog face in my office door.

I wearily stood up and swung open the door. To my relief, there stood an older gentleman in a stiff woolen suit. He had to be at least 80.

"Hello," I said, putting on a pleasant smile.

"Hello." He held out his hand. "I am Arthur Gottlieb."

"Nice to meet you, Mr. Gottlieb. I am Professor Rasmussen." I shook his hand. "What can I do for you?" I asked.

"It is what I can do for you," he said with a slight accent. "May I come in?" He motioned with the cane that he gripped in his left hand.

I hesitated for just an instant, considering the work I needed to do. But curiosity won out.

"Please." I waved him to the wooden chair I reserved for students. The less comfortable the chair, the less time they spent in my office. I seated myself back behind my desk.

"So what can you do for me?" I asked, as I reached for my coffee and took a sip.

He leaned forward conspiratorially. "I have discovered a mathematical proof of God."

I coughed up the coffee.

"Excuse me?"

"I have a mathematical proof of God." He nodded knowingly.

I laughed nervously. Bunsen was starting to look a whole lot better.

"Um, I'm sorry," I said, "but you can't have a mathematical proof of God. God is not defined as a mathematical object about which you can prove theorems. Just like you can't have a mathematical proof there are atoms. Atoms and God, if they exist, are attributes of the real world. Math is just about math."

"Well I have a proof," he said with finality, sitting back in his chair.

I sighed and settled back in my own chair. It didn't look like he was planning on leaving soon.

"Okay," I said. "I'll bite. How does it go?"

He smiled slightly and lifted his eyebrows. "It is a proof by contradiction."

"Yeah?" I said, flicking a glance at my computer, wondering if I had any new email.

"Yes, I assume first of all that there is no God and then ultimately I derive a contradiction. Therefore there must be a God."

"And what is the contradiction?"

"That my first wife's name was Gladys."

"That's ridiculous."

"Yes, it is. My first wife's name was Elba. It was my second wife who was named Gladys."

"No, I mean that's not the kind of contradiction you get out of a mathematical proof. You have to get a mathematical contradiction like A is strictly greater than B and B is strictly greater than A. Or like $1 = 2$."

"But I have $1 = 2$. I show that my first wife, wife number one, is named Gladys, but that is actually the name of my second wife, wife number 2. So $1 = 2$."

"Okay, fine. But my point is that things like your wives' names shouldn't come up in a mathematical proof. Mathematical proofs should be about mathematical objects, like numbers, groups, algebras, topologies. Gladys and Elba are not mathematical objects."

"They are elements of the set of all wives that I have had."

"Sure."

"Then they are mathematical objects."

I sighed. "Okay, sure. So they are mathematical objects. And so you use them to show that God exists."

He glanced over at my open door and then leaned forward again. "Actually, that is only one of the things I prove."

"Really?" I said." Pray tell, what else do you prove?"

"I prove that the parallel postulate follows from Euclid's other axioms. I provide an algorithm for trisecting any angle. I give a formula for finding the roots of a fifth degree polynomial."

I threw up my hands. "What? You don't square the circle?"

"What does that mean?"

"The one you left out, squaring the circle. It means constructing with straightedge and compass a square that has area exactly equal to the area of a unit circle, which is π."

"Oh, I can do that, too."

I whistled. "You are quite a piece of work."

"Thank you," he said, smiling.

"Okay," I said. "Now tell me. Does it bother you that all of these results, trisecting the angle, showing that the parallel postulate follows from the other axioms, giving a formula for the roots of a fifth degree polynomial, they are all known to be false?"

"If you mean that others have claimed to prove them false, I am aware of that."

"And it doesn't bother you that mathematicians all over the world have accepted those proofs as correct?

"Mathematics is not a democracy."

Now I was exasperated. "No, it's not. But the whole idea of a proof in mathematics is that it can be checked by any reasonable human being, and the conclusion will be that it is correct. A whole heck of a lot of human beings have looked at the proofs of these results, and come to the same conclusion; they are correct."

"Yes, but these same human beings don't understand algebraic lingerie."

"Excuse me. Did you say lingerie?"

"Yes, they are mathematical objects related to the set of all wives that I have ever had. I created them."

I looked out my door to see if there was anyone in the hall in case I needed help.

"You see," he continued. "Algebraic lingerie helps to contain sets such as the set of all wives I have ever had. It is a meta set, used to restrain unruly subsets of the original set."

Suddenly I was paying attention. Dickson had suggested the possibility of such sets in the 1930s but nothing had ever come of the idea.

"How would these meta sets help you in your argument?" I asked, trying not to let on my interest.

"The algebraic lingerie allows the creation of a homomorphism from the set of all names to the set of all wives that I have ever had. Assuming the nonexistence of God, one can infer that names are not determined by a higher design. Therefore, some probability distribution governs their choice. Applying a Poisson process, one generates a homogeneous Markov chain."

"Wait a minute," I said. "Why homogeneous? Isn't nonhomogeneity implied by the transitivity of the Laplacian?"

"Only when the process is semi-simple. When the process is simple, as in our case, the Laplacian is only defined over a compact subdomain, and its transitivity there doesn't even imply superellipticity, let alone homogeneity."

"Oh." I didn't know where this was going, but it was clear the guy knew some math. "Please continue."

"Well, then we factor by the kernel of the homomorphism, yielding an abstract subvariety determined by the maximal ideal. The definition of this subvariety can be analytically continued and then completed to yield a simplicial complex in a fundamental domain for the action of the cusp subgroup of a hyperbolic orbifold commensurable with a Bianchi group of arbirarily large discriminant. The trace field generates a dilogarithmic map that lifts to the universal cover. Quotienting out by the orientation-reversing isometries yields a manifold of Hausdorff dimension $3/2$. The cohomological sheaf of this manifold allows us to prove the existence of a bilocal diffeomorphsim onto the generators for the fundamental group of a CR-manifold of dimension 12. The primary obstruction to a lifting of the associated Steenrod algebra affords a means to define a weakly contractible map to the commutator. Suspending this map yields a cofibration of the associated Eilenberg-MacLane space. Taking the one-point compactification under the Zariski topology generates a moduli space that parametrizes the finitely generated quasi-Fuchsian groups of rank one. If we restrict to codimension three, we obtain an excellent ring, the localization of which is a factor field. Projecting to the generic fiber yields a Lipshitz map from the set of names to the set of all wives. When the range is restricted to just my wives, the commutativity of the map forces my first wife to have the name Gladys. And that is a contradiction."

He thumped his cane on the floor for emphasis. I sat open mouthed. Everything he had said made sense. I had just heard the single most important mathematical exposition in the history of mathematics, bar none. This guy made Gauss look like a ditchdigger. I needed to stall while I figured out what to do.

"The. . . ummm. . . the Steenrod algebra. How do you get its primary obstruction?"

"The algebra is defined in terms of a generating set that depends only on the tangential bifurcation present in the extreme values corresponding to the compact core. If there were not a primary obstruction, then transitivity would not hold in its cofinite extension. But the cofinite extension is Hopfian by definition and hence transitivity must hold." He thumped his cane again.

"Oh, yes, I see," I said, although in truth, I would need a month to figure out his answer. "Now tell me. Have you told your proof to anyone else?"

"No," he said. "I am no longer married. My fifth wife, Henrietta, she passed away three years ago. So I decided, five wives, it is enough. Now I turn to mathematics. I work for three years. But you are the first person to whom I tell my proof."

"I see." I stood up and swung the door to my office closed. "Wouldn't want the wrong person listening in," I said with a smile. He brightened considerably, assuming I now believed him.

I sat back down and leaned forward, placing my elbows on the desk.

"Mr. Gottlieb, I appreciate your coming by. It is inspiring to see such a vigorous interest in mathematics. And certainly you have absorbed a lot of, shall we say, background."

He tipped his head in acknowledgement.

"But nowadays, Mr. Gottlieb, original mathematics cannot be produced by amateurs. It takes years of study to reach the level of understanding necessary. Math is just too abstract."

"But I have done it," he said, his eyebrows furrowing. "I just explained it to you."

"Mr. Gottlieb," I said firmly, "although much of what you said would sound reasonable to a layperson, to a mathematician such as myself it is clearly nonsense. You haven't proved anything here. You've merely tied together a string of words that sound plausible, but in fact mean no more than a nursery rhyme. I suggest you go home, and find a more productive pasttime. Perhaps you might enjoy watching TV."

Gottlieb turned red in the face.

"What are you saying?" he said in a trembling voice. "You know I am right. Why do you deny it?"

"In fact, Mr. Gottlieb, I know you are wrong. You claim to have disproved some of the most well-known and fundamental results in mathematics, let alone your claim of a proof of God. If you were right, well, all of mathematics as we know it would come tumbling down, and the public would lose confidence in the mathematical community. I am sorry. I am a busy man, and I don't have time to listen to a demented old man who makes up mathematics to distract himself from his grief over the loss of a long chain of wives."

Gottlieb stood up, waving his cane. Veins stood out prominently on his forehead.

"How dare you," he cried. "How dare you speak to me in this manner!" His face was bright red now, and he was glaring at me.

Suddenly, he clawed at his chest. "I...I..."

For an instant, he looked surprised. Then he crumpled to the floor, his cane bouncing off the file cabinet and clattering down beside him. I rushed around the desk and lifted his head onto my knee. He looked up at me, his face ashen. "Tell me the truth," he said. "You know I proved it."

I hesitated for a second. Then I said, "Yes, you proved it."

"God exists. You know it. You must live with it." Then his head fell back, and I knew he was dead.

I slumped back down to the floor, his head still resting in my lap. Here was perhaps the greatest mathematician of all time, and I was the only person who knew it. Because of me and my actions, he was dead. I carefully lifted his head from my lap and placed it gently on the floor. Then I called security.

I won the Cole prize two years later. It was for work on algebraic lingerie. I could have announced any one of the results, and it would have been enough to guarantee me instant fame, but I was careful not to undermine too much of mathematics at once. I didn't want to put myself and every other mathematician out of work. Better to leak the results one at a time, and hope the underlying mathematical framework would recuperate between blows.

My renown spread quickly. I flew from one invited address to another. Mathematicians flocked to my talks.

About once a year, I announced another result. Each time, it was as if someone had kicked the mathematical anthill, with all the mathematicians scurrying to repair the damage. Each time, my stock rose accordingly.

I considered announcing the proof of God as the coup de grace, but couldn't bring myself to do so. Initially, I reasoned that it wouldn't make the world a better place. There are more than enough people already convinced there is a God and happy to kill one another because of it. Perhaps it is just as well to let everyone make up their own minds.

But ultimately, I realized this was a rationalization on my part. My reluctance came more from the sense that claiming a proof of God as my own would be a sacrilege an order of magnitude greater than I had already committed. Somebody was keeping accounts, and my tally wasn't looking so good.

It didn't take long before I stopped enjoying the attention. The question of my ultimate accountability was always there, nagging me in the background.

I stopped accepting invitations to speak, and began to avoid my colleagues, skipping department meetings and seminars, claiming I was too busy with my work. No one dared complain.

So now, I find myself spending the days sitting in my office with the door closed. Once in a while I work through the implications of Gottlieb's work, and I realize some other basic tenet of mathematics is incorrect, and I see the further disintegration of the mathematical machinery that took thousands of years to build.

I no longer work on my own mathematics, which I once enjoyed so much. What is the point? None of the results would compare to the results for which I am already famous. Nobody would care. And anyway, the mathematical scaffolding upon which they would depend is itself corrupt.

No, most of the time, I just sit, staring at a blank pad on my desk. I sit and I stare, trying not to think about what I have done, trying not to think about anything, always under the watchful eye of God.

The Red Badge
of Courage

I remember that day as if it were yesterday. I will never forget it. Often, I wake up at night, in sweat-soaked sheets, screaming "Look out Sarge, look out!" Often my roommate is screaming, too. "Shut up, shut up!" But I can't shut up. I have to tell the story, the story of that fateful day. A day that can never be forgotten.

We were fresh out of boot camp, Leftie and me. Hardly knew an integral from a derivative. We thought the power rule was complicated. Just a pair of snot-nosed calc students. But they said we were ready for Calc II. How ridiculous that sounds now.

We arrived in the country and were assigned to a unit of misfits. Sarge was the only one of us who had seen real combat before. She had fought in WWW I, a web-based trig course. And then there was Pipsqueak, Pops, Leftie, and me. They called me Kodowski. I wanted them to call me Trixie. But they refused.

Before we had even finished unpacking our gear, we heard a yell. "Incoming!" Grunts dove for cover. Sarge just kept eating her granola bar. "Relax," she said. "It's just a quiz." I stayed low anyway. It seemed dangerous enough to me. But it wouldn't be long before I understood the difference.

I remember that fateful morning as if it were yesterday. I woke to something dripping on my forehead. Leftie had wet the upper bunk again. He gave new meaning to the words math anxiety. I pulled him off his bunk and we had a quick shoving match. Then we threw on our uniforms. No time to brush teeth or comb hair. Ours or anybody else's. Destiny waits for no one. As we stumbled toward the front line, ominous clouds hung low in the sky.

We found the rest of the unit near the frontline. Pipsqueak looked like she was going to lose her breakfast, and Pops' hands were shaking. (He was a continuing ed student.) Sarge munched on a Pop-Tart nonchalantly. Was she really that unconcerned or was that the impression she wanted us to have? I didn't know for sure, but the Pop-Tart sure looked good.

As we spread out over the lecture hall hunkering down in our foxholes, I felt queasy myself. This was it. The real thing. no more training sessions with dummy problems whizzing overhead, and a solutions manual available for cover. This would be live ammunition exploding around us. Everyone else looked as frightened as I felt. Now, we find out what you're made of, I thought to myself, as the hour struck and the general down front signaled the beginning of the battle. I gulped once and turned over the cover page.

A couple of partial derivatives whistled overhead, and I thought to myself, I can handle this. I started firing, plugged a couple quick. Hey, no worse than an afternoon of video games, I said to myself.

Then I came up over the next page, and swallowed hard as I found myself face-to-face with an armored series division. I didn't even stop to think. I just peppered them with Ratio Tests. A few went up in flames. The rest rolled forward. I switched to Root Tests, spraying them indiscriminantly. A couple more went down but the rest rumbled forward. So I lobbed in a couple of Basic Comparison Tests and a Limit Comparison Test or two. Then I let loose with the Alternating Series Test and followed up with half a ton of nth-term tests. That ought to do it, I thought as I waited for the smoke to clear. But among the littered carcasses on the field before me, there still stood one lone series. At first I couldn't make it out. But as it lumbered forward, I suddenly realized what this monstrosity must be. It was the dreaded harmonic series. It looked right at me and then let out a howl that turned my bowels to ice.

How do you stop the harmonic series? I tried desperately to remember. We had talked about this in basic training. My instructor's voice echoed in my head, "Pray you never see a harmonic series in battle. They are the nastiest, the ugliest series you will ever see. They diverge, but just barely. There is only one thing to do if you ever find yourself looking down the barrel of the harmonic series...." Yes, yes, I thought, as I waited for the voice to finish its explanation. "Use the integral test."

"See you in hell," I screamed as I pulled the trigger. The series blew into a million pieces. I laughed maniacally. "Now that's what I call a divergent series."

Soldiers in adjacent foxholes said, "Shhh," and the general down front gave me a concerned look. I turned the page, and took a triple integral right in the gut. I rolled out of my seat and down three steps of the auditorium stairs. A medic, must have been a TA no more than 22 years old, rushed over.

"Are you all right?" she asked, a concerned look on her face.

I felt for the wound in my belly, but miraculously, my hand came out clean. "It must have hit me in the belt buckle," I said as she helped me to my feet. She handed me my helmet and gave me a strange look. She was probably wondering how anyone could survive a triple integral. But stranger things have happened. I retook my seat.

There was a noise behind me. I looked around just in time to see Leftie turning tail and heading for the exit. "Leftie, get back here," I yelled. "They'll court martial you for sure."

The neighboring soldiers shushed me again. Afraid I would attract ordinance. I should have known Leftie wouldn't have the guts for it. Ever since that quiz problem on improper integrals, he had had the shakes.

I leaned over the exam and a word problem went off right in my face, something about length plus girth of a package at the post office. There was red ink everywhere. I waved the medic over and pointed at the problem, but she said, "I'm sorry. I can't help you." I guess there were grunts hurt worse than me. I pulled off my helmet and tied a bandana around my head. It was a sea of red ink out there. The noise was deafening. I started working on the problem in spite of the pain.

At one point, I happened to glance over at the Sarge. She didn't look right. I gave her the thumbs up sign, but she didn't respond. She looked like she might be sick. She was slumped down in her seat. I couldn't see it, but I had to assume there was a pool of red ink on the exam in front of her. I realized she must have taken one in the gut.

She was the one who had come up with my nickname, Kodowski. Granted it was my last name, but it had meant a lot to me the first time she called me that. She had saved my ass at least a dozen times already. And now I was losing her, and there was nothing I could do about it. The frustration welled up inside me, and suddenly I roared. Something inside me snapped. I was no longer a human being. I was a calculus-killing machine. I flipped the page and mowed down eight partial derivatives. I turned around and nailed three limit problems before they even saw me. I took out a triple integral in cylindrical coordinates. Nothing could stop me. Three chain-rule problems turned to run, but I never gave them the chance. I flipped page after page, charging forward. I was singlehandedly turning the tide. Suddenly I realized the battle was almost over. I triumphantly flipped the last page and found myself face-to-face with the nastiest triple integral problem I had ever seen. It was a volume inside a sphere but outside a cylinder; the famous cored apple. But it said to do it in spherical coordinates. You have to be kidding, I thought to myself. What twisted, devious mind would create such a diabolical weapon? I had no idea what to do.

But then I remembered Sarge's words. "You can't come at a problem like that directly. Come at it from below. One step at a time."

"Yeah, Sarge, I remember," I said out loud. I first figured out the equations for the sphere and the cylinder in spherical coordinates.

One step in front of the other, Sarge. Then I looked at the intersection. "It's described by an angle, Sarge, I know." I wrote down the triple integral. Sarge's words echoing in my ears. "Don't forget. $\rho^2 \sin \varphi \, d\rho \, d\varphi \, d\theta$ in the integrand."

Don't worry, Sarge. I won't forget that for as long as I live.

And then it came down to just pulling the trigger. The integral could essentially do itself. I circled my answer in bright purple ink. Then I flipped the exam closed, stood, and walked down to the front of the room. The general looked at me nervously.

"Are you proud of yourself?" I said. "All these young lives, wasted. Littered on the field of battle. Never again to raise a pencil for mathematics. Do you feel good about that?"

He looked confused.

"Here is your stinking exam," I said as I threw it down on the table. He stood open-mouthed as I turned and walked up the steps.

We lost them all that day, Sarge, Pipsqueak, Pops, and Leftie. They became Psych majors. I still see them in the halls sometimes, but they never meet my gaze. The math walking wounded.

I was awarded the silver cross to hang on my A, making it an A+. I was promoted, too. They made me a grader. They wanted me to go to officer's training school at Princeton or maybe Berkeley. And maybe someday I will. Maybe that would make it all worthwhile. But I have to get over the nightmares first. I have to reconcile my victory with the loss of my friends. I have to see mathematics as a tool for good, not a weapon of destruction. Then, and only then, will I be able to move on.

This Theorem is Big

Hey, Barry. It's me, Sid. Listen, I just had to call you, because I have a theorem like no other theorem you ever saw. You are going to go apeship over this. This one is going to be big. And not just a little big. We are talking another Atiyah-Patodi-Singer Index Theorem. Think Mostow Rigidity or Heine-Borel. This is mega blockbuster material.

I'm shopping it around and let me tell you, there's a lot of interest. But I wanted you to have a shot at it. I know you guys haven't had a big hit in a while, not since Riemann-Roch. So I know you're hungry. This one has the potential to be a blockbuster.

Get ready, because here it is. The Mandelbrot-Thurston-Wiles Pi-Orbifold Syzygy Theorem. How about that, huh?

You don't get more star power than Mandelbrot, Thurston, and Wiles. These are box-office heavies. And if you're picking a real number to put in the title of a theorem, you can't get hotter than π.

And hell, we have a word in there whose only vowel is y AND it appears three times. This word is so end-of-the alphabet heavy, it screams brilliance.

Now you are probably wondering how I got these three big names to agree to this project. And the honest truth is that I don't yet have them all on board. But this is where you come in. The only reason they are hesitating is the need for a sponsoring institution, a place of your caliber. They aren't going to sign on with some community college with a 4-4 teaching load. No, they need to know that you're going to provide the resources necessary for this theorem to get the attention it deserves. Let me tell you what I have in mind.

I want you to get invitations for all three to speak at the Institute for Advanced Study, The Fields Institute, and at the International Congress. I'm betting you can make that happen. That's why I called you. And I'm thinking there should be some awards from some wealthy Middle Eastern countries. Or maybe Japan. You may have to pull some strings, but I'm betting you can do that. I'm thinking big gold ingots, with a picture of Gauss stamped on them, or maybe a big belt, like they give out at the World Wrestling Federation.

On the PR front, we have lots of ideas. We're thinking of spicing things up a bit, having a shoving match between Thurston and Wiles at the AMS meetings, all faked of course. But imagine the PR potential. Stars not getting along. Disagreement over the credit for the corollaries. This is hot stuff. We'll get the front page of the tabloids.

And of course, there will be the love interest. Get this. Thurston, dyed in the wool topologist, right? He falls for analytic number theory. See? So that's what he contributes to the theorem. But, then, there is some lemma trouble. ANT's pretty rigid stuff. Thurston's frustrated. Thinking maybe he's made a mistake. Misses his old sweetheart, topology. She was supple, forgiving. But in the end, the lemmas work out, and love transcends all. I'm telling you, there won't be a dry eye in the house.

You're probably wondering what the theorem will say. Me, too. Quite frankly, I haven't got a clue. But I haven't brought the writers on board yet. I'm thinking maybe it will have to do with the structure of singularities. Yeah, that has a ring to it. But there won't be three or four singularities, there will be π of them. Yeah, an irrational number of them. We'll generalize the very definition of cardinality of sets. And we'll have a sequence. No, a lot of sequences. Wait, wait, make those spectral sequences. Bockstein spectral sequences. And they are converging to other spectral sequences. Grothendieck spectral sequences. And the indices on the sequences are themselves sequences. And there's a tower of these sequences reaching way up into the sky.

And there will be some incompleteness. Say a Cauchy sequence that doesn't converge. Or a statement that is true but unproveable. Yeah, but get this. The co-authors don't care. They prove it anyway. Wow, this is good. But of course, we're still in the early development stages. We'll need Mandelbrot, Thurston, and Wiles to fill in some of the details.

Oh, and the theorem will have implications. Oh yes, will it ever have implications. It will certainly imply the Riemann Hypothesis at the very least. Maybe Poincaré, and Goldbach, too. And it will show the airlines how to distribute their planes to the airports to maximize their profit. Maybe then the President could thank the three authors in a special televised address to the nation, with a whole lot of happy pilots standing behind him. Oh, this is good. Anyway, let me know what you think. We have to move on this fast, before someone else does it. Who knows, if we play this theorem right, maybe Ron Howard will make it into a movie. Sorry for the long message. Call me.

Journey to the Center
of Mathematics

It was only 2:00 in the afternoon on a Thursday when I heard the front door to our little house on the Königstrasse slam.

"Axle, come at once," called Professor Lederhosen, as he rushed through the entry into his study. The professor was not a patient man, so I thrust my Jules Verne novel under the covers, leapt up from the bed and descended the stairs. Timidly, I poked my head inside the door to his sanctuary.

"Axle, see this amazing book I have purchased," he exclaimed with his characteristic fervor. "It is a 12th-century tome, entirely written in runic characters." He proferred a well-thumbed text bound in worn leather.

"Quite a find, professor," I answered, feigning interest. "And now, I shall return to my chores."

"No nephew, you do not understand. This is the long lost book of Icelandic doggerel verse. This completes my collection of doggerel verses of the world." As he spoke these words, a small piece of parchment slipped from the book and floated to the floor.

"What could this be?" he exclaimed, as he reached down to pick it up.

"A meaningless scrap, perhaps," I replied hopefully.

"Oh, Axle, I doubt very much that a 12th-century book of Icelandic doggerel verse would contain a meaningless scrap of paper."

He lifted the piece to within an inch of his nose and squinted.

"Why, this appears to have also been written in runic characters. Either that or it was written by a chicken."

I laughed aloud, only to stifle myself the instant I realized he was not joking.

"Who could have written this?" demanded the professor. "And what could it mean?"

"Perhaps it was written by the owner of the book," I said. "It says here on the inside cover 'This book belongs to Arnold Sackmuffin.'"

"Sackmuffin! It cannot be," said my uncle, his face turning ashen.

"Why? Who is Arnold Sackmuffin?"

"Axle, are you a complete illiterate? Only perhaps the greatest savant of Iceland during the years 1655-1659. He must have written this message."

"How can we figure out what it means?" I asked.

"In fact, Axle, I took runic as a schoolboy. It was that or wood shop. I would wager that I can still translate with the best of them."

The professor proceeded to sit down at the table and slowly transcribe one letter after the other. Upon finishing, he stood slowly and read the result. "Plump dishes pinch the waffle man."

"What could this possibly mean?" he wailed. "Dishes cannot pinch anyone."

"Wait, Uncle," I exclaimed. "Flip it over and read it again."

As he did so, I stared over his shoulder, dumbfounded at the decrypted message that could now be read on the parchment.

"Descend if you dare into the crater of Sard's Theorem and you will attain the center of mathematics; which I have already done– Arnold Sackmuffin."

"The center of mathematics!" exclaimed the professor as he fell into his chair, which immediately tipped over backward, sending him crashing to the floor. As I helped my uncle to his feet, I asked him what was this Sard's Theorem.

"Oh, Axle, for a student of mathematics, you know perilously little mathematics," he replied. "Sard's Theorem is the central mountain of differential topology. An inactive volcano, it can only be reached by a long slog through the desert of Differential Topology."

This was beginning to sound ominous.

"Well, this has all been fascinating, professor. And now I shall return to my work."

"My dear nephew, don't you see? We have discovered the secret of how to reach the center of mathematics, how to travel to its very core. This is an amazing revelation. We must prepare to leave at once."

"But I do not want to go. Honestly, Uncle, I do not understand mathematics. And I do not think I have what it takes to be a mathematician."

"All the more reason to go, my boy. We will learn from whence it comes. We will travel to its very source. And then perhaps, you will understand. Perhaps we will all understand."

"Very well, Uncle. I know there is no use in arguing with you. When do we start?"

"We leave tomorrow. But first we must gather up the necessary supplies and find a guide. Grab those textbooks off the shelf there. Dump them in this bag."

The next day, we booked travel on a steamer across the Analytic Ocean. All too soon, we found ourselves trudging through the desolate wasteland of Differential Topology following our newly hired guide, Hansel, a mathematician from Stockholm who spoke neither English nor Swedish. But he was quite good with hand signals.

Several weeks did it take us to cross the desert. Much did I learn on that journey. I learned that the tangent space at a point to an m-dimensional smooth manifold is a vector space. I learned that a nonsingular derivative at a point x of a smooth map f from R^n to R^n implies that f sends a neighborhood of x diffeomorphically onto a neighborhood of $f(x)$. I learned not to share a pillow with

Professor Lederhosen, as he drools in his sleep. Finally, after many tortuous days of slow progress, we found ourselves at the foot of Sard's Theorem.

I looked up at the immense cone of the volcano that lay high above us.

"We must climb that?" I asked.

"Fear not, Axle," replied the professor. "First we sleep. Then in the morning we attack Sard."

When I woke the next morning, Hansel had already packed the gear. Unable to communicate verbally, he was busily kicking me awake.

"Come, sleepyhead," called the professor, obviously eager to begin the climb. "It is time for us to learn some mathematics."

Seven hours later, we stood on the crest of the crater, looking down into the darkened craw of the mountain.

A rock on the rim caught the professor's attention. "See here," he called excitedly. "This symbol hacked into the stone: '∞'. That is the mark of Sackmuffin. This must be the way down."

We threaded our way through a field of boulders the size of cottages, as we descended into the crater. Eventually we arrived at a ledge from which darkness was all we could see below.

"There is no way further down," I said to the professor. "Too bad. This has been exciting, but now we must return home."

"Nonsense, Axle, have you never before become entangled in a proof, unable to continue forward? Do you just give up? Do you throw in the towel?"

"Yes, professor, that is what I do."

"That is why you are not yet a mathematician, my boy. We will make one of you yet."

"Do not concern yourself with me, professor. I am happy the way I am."

My uncle ignored me.

"We continue down. All we need is our ropes and ingenuity." Ten minutes later, I found myself dangling from the ledge by a rope, as I was lowered slowly into the depths of the very core of the silent volcano. As I turned on my electric light, I could see the details of the proof of Sard's Theorem. Here was Fubini's Theorem, which is critical in the proof. And there was the descending sequence of closed sets that form the core of Sard's Theorem.

As I looked back up toward the professor and Hansel above me, I could see the light of the outside world dwindling quickly. By the time I reached the bottom, signs of the surface could no longer reach me. Within the hour, all three of us stood in the small well of light made by my electric lantern.

"Now what, Professor?" I asked.

"See, here, Axle. The mark of Sackmuffin on the wall of this passage. Follow me." He took the light from my hand and proceeded down the passage. Hansel followed. I quickly took up the rear, not wanting to be left behind in the descending darkness with the fearsome matrices of partial derivatives that surrounded me.

For several days, we traveled deeper and deeper into the heart of mathematics. From differential topology, we entered the world of point set topology. Many a beautiful basis we passed sparkling in the reflected light from our electric lanterns. Pathological topologies of complexity too twisted to describe appeared before our eyes. If I had only had the time and courage to write it all down, I would have had many a research paper to my name.

After several days of downhill travel, I noticed the passageway had taken on a distinct upward incline. The mathematics around us was no longer becoming simpler as we traveled forward. Rather, it was taking on an ominous complexity. This continued for a few hours until I could contain my concern no longer.

"Professor, we are not getting closer to the center of mathematics. We are getting farther away with each step."

"You are more discerning than I would have given you credit for, my boy. Our path has taken us into algebraic topology. It appears we will have to continue upward for the time being. I have every hope that the path will crest soon."

I looked with dread upon the tunnel wall, where I saw Čech cohomology groups with coefficients in presheaves. As we continued, we soon found ourselves in the midst of the Relative Hurewicz Isomorphism Theorem. Turning a bend, I saw what appeared to be a Leray-Serre spectral sequence. This was too much for me.

"Uncle, I beseech you. We must turn back. We cannot go on this way. If I am not mistaken, we are now deeply enmeshed in the field of Homotopy Theory. If we continue, we will just become more entangled in this morass and we shall never find our way out."

The professor turned to me, flashing the light directly into my eyes.

"Axle, what if Norman Steenrod had reacted this way when he first confronted homotopy theory? What if J.H.C. Whitehead had turned tail and run when he came face-to-face with absolute neighborhood retracts? What if Heinz Hopf had buried his head in the sand when he discovered hopficity?"

I motioned to the fiber bundles hanging from the ceiling and jutting up out of the floor.

"But professor, look at our surroundings. We cannot possibly hope to understand what is going on here, let alone anything more complicated."

"Axle, at this point, we have no choice. We have come too far to go back. Our water supply will not last long enough for us to return the way we have come. We must continue in the hopes of finding water. Do not be frightened by a few fiber bundles. I am certain the path will level off soon, and then begin its descent anew."

We continued along the passage for several more hours, my throat becoming more parched with each step. I ached for just a sip of water. But Hansel guarded the water supply zealously, and warned me off with guttural threats and vigorous hand gestures whenever I grabbed for the canteen. When I had finally given up all hope, and was just looking for a comfortable spot to lay down, the path did level off. And then it began to descend. I saw an Eilenberg-MacLane space embedded in the wall. And there was some homology with Z coefficients. My flagging spirits rose concommitent with the descent in our altitude. Then suddenly, the passageway opened up into a huge cavern, from the far end of which there appeared a blue-green luminescence. As we crossed the broad cavern floor, approaching this strange light, the stone at our feet was replaced with sand. I could feel a breeze blowing moist air across my face. I began to run, my colleagues just behind me, until the vista opened upon a miraculous sight. It was a giant underworld ocean extending indefinitely beyond the horizon.

"What could this be?" I asked, as the three of us stood awestruck on the sandy beach, waves lapping at our toes.

"It is Morse Theory," replied the professor.

"Thank God for it, whatever it is," I said, as I fell down on the sand and submerged my head in the water, drinking greedily.

After replenishing ourselves and resting by the shore, we wandered down the beach until we came across a grove of logarithms growing out of the sand. Cutting them down, we lashed them together to construct a raft. Shortly, we found ourselves on the Morse Sea, making good time as a strong breeze blew our makeshift sail. Hansel steered us with a rudder we had attached to the stern.

Quickly, the shoreline receded in the distance, and all that filled our horizon was water in every direction. The cavern ceiling was so far above us that we could no longer make it out through the hazy clouds floating overhead. The water itself gave off the luminescent light that illuminated this underworld ocean.

After three days of sailing, there appeared a large land mass rising up out of the water. As we approached, we recognized it to be an island, with a peak rising up out of the water and disappearing into the clouds overhead.

"Do you know it, professor?" "Yes, Axle, it can only be Mazur's Theorem, which uses Morse theory to prove that a smoothly embedded n-dimensional sphere sitting inside an $(n+1)$-dimensional sphere always separates it into two $(n+1)$-dimensional balls."

I stared up at its inspiring cliffs, and then watched it sink into the horizon behind us, once again leaving us alone in the flat expanse of water. Suddenly Hansel started to gesticulate excitedly, pointing ahead of us. We saw darkening clouds approaching from the west. The wind began to pick up.

"It appears we are in for some weather," said the professor calmly.

"But, Uncle, from whence would come weather on an ocean deep in the interior of mathematics?"

"Perhaps some logical inconsistencies are passing through the bowels, inconsistencies that are causing indigestion and that may require some adjustments to accommodate."

I was not sure to what extent his digestive analogy was meant to be taken literally. I preferred to think of mathematics as an inanimate object rather than a living breathing creature that was having stomach trouble.

The howl of the wind picked up, and my uncle's further words were lost in the tumult that descended upon us. Our tiny craft was tossed upon towering waves, as we clung to the mast. The temperature dropped by 30 degrees. Rain, flying horizontally, soaked us to the core. Hansel grabbed a rope with his free hand, and tied us to the mast. I watched with horror as the rucksack containing our provisions was washed overboard. The storm continued unabated for two days. At some point I lost consciousness, slumped against the mast.

I was lying on a beach, face in the sand, when I regained my senses. It was the sound of good old Hansel yelling gibberish that convinced me that I lived still. Looking up, I saw him pointing to an opening in the rock wall at the end of the beach. Even from a distance I could make out the mark of Sackmuffin chiseled into the stone.

We gathered the belongings that had survived our voyage and set off down the passage. Almost at once we came to the end of the tunnel. We were face-to-face with a complicated counterexample that had somehow become dislodged from the roof of the tunnel, and fallen down to block our way.

"Professor, this is a dead end."

"Yes, nephew, this must have fallen down since Sackmuffin passed this way, perhaps even during this last storm."

"But what can we do? Is this the end of our journey?"

"Do not give up yet, my boy. We will have to blast our way through."

"How do we do that?"

He reached into his rucksack. "I brought along a few axioms that should do the trick. That counterexample will cease to exist if we change the axioms. It will be reduced to rubble."

My uncle dropped to his knees and with his hands, dug a small hole underneath the counterexample. Then he gingerly squeezed the axioms in. Pushing in the end of a fuse, he then unrolled it until we were again standing on the beach, one hundred yards away.

"Axle, would you like to do the honors?" he asked, offering me a match. I struck it on the sole of my shoe and lit the fuse.

"Quickly," he said. "Get on the raft. We can float out another hundred feet for safety."

Just as we had pushed off the beach, there was a deafening roar. Rocks shot out of the tunnel and cascaded around us. A large wave lifted us up in the air, as the rock wall in front of us crumbled.

"Those axioms seem to be doing a bit more damage than I had expected," yelled the professor.

A huge crevasse opened in the beach and the ocean began to pour in, sweeping us with it. We found ourselves shooting down a large opening, riding the wave at the front of a massive moving body of water.

"Hang on," yelled my uncle as the water swirled about us, and we rocketed down the passageway.

I glanced at the mathematics whizzing by and my heart leapt.

"Look professor, sines and cosines. It is trigonometry! We must be getting close."

We passed through high school algebra, word problems, and exponents. And then up ahead was an outcropping of rock by an opening in the rock wall. It was the side-angle-side theorem from geometry.

"Axle, steer the raft toward that theorem and get ready to jump," yelled the professor. "This may be our only chance."

At the last possible second, we leapt for the rocks. The raft careened off the theorem and splintered into pieces. The three of us pulled ourselves to safety, sitting on the lip of a small proof about parallelograms. The water continued to rush by. I turned to see where we were and there on the wall above us was the mark of Sackmuffin.

I leapt to my feet.

"We must be almost there," I exclaimed as I started down the passage. Hansel and my uncle got up to follow. I found myself in the midst of arithmetic. Good old arithmetic. Even I could do arithmetic. Adding fractions, long division, multiplying three-digit numbers.

Grinning from ear to ear, I continued down the passage as the surrounding equations became even simpler. Here was the multiplication table for integers less than ten and here was addition of small numbers. This must be it, I thought. I am almost there. I turned the corner, pointing my light ahead of me and stopped dead.

I stood dumbfounded as I stared at the center of mathematics. Was it algebra? Was it topology? Was it number theory? None of the above. In fact none of anything. There was nothing there.

Hansel and the professor collided with me as they rushed around the corner.

"How can this be, Professor?" I asked plaintively. Hansel waved desperate hand signals.

The professor stood silently, his brow creased in thought.

"Professor, there is nothing here. The center of mathematics is empty."

Suddenly the professor looked up, a smile on his face.

"Ah, Axle, that is the answer. There is nothing here, because that is how you create the numbers, from nothing."

"What do you mean?"

"First there is nothing. That is the set $\emptyset$, the empty set."

"Yes, I see we have the empty set here. Since there is nothing here."

"But Axle, now we have something. A set that is empty."

"What do you mean?"

"We now have something. It is the set called the empty set."

"Yes, but it isn't there."

"Oh, it assuredly is there. It is something, is it not? It is a set."

"Yes, it is a set."

"Isn't a set something?"

"Yes. . . ."

"So now we have created something! Something from nothing. Does it not make you feel like a god?"

"Not particularly. And what about the rest of mathematics? Now, we have just one set, a set which contains no elements."

"Yes, but you see, my boy, now we can take the set that has this set as an element. This is a nonempty set. It contains one element which is this set. We write it like this." With the toe of his boot, he drew a picture in the sand at my feet: '$\{\emptyset\}$'

"Sounds a bit self-referential to me."

"So what? Then we have the set that consists of the empty set, and the set that has an element, the empty set. This forms a two-element set $\{\{\emptyset\}, \emptyset\}$."

"You are making my head spin, Professor. I need to sit down."

But as I went to do so, the ground upon which I desired to sit began to move. A low grumble echoed through the chamber.

"I fear, Axle," said the professor, "that in stating the solution to this puzzle, we have set in motion powers beyond our ability to comprehend. Run!"

The ground began to shake and split. Steam shot up out of the cracks that were forming.

"Quick, into this lemma," yelled the professor. He leaped over the edge, pulling me with him. Hansel jumped in after us, just as there was a deafening roar. Logical arguments burst around us. The lemma was thrown upward with incredible force, the three of us holding on for dear life. As the pent-up forces exploded, we found ourselves being blown up a large crack in the rock that had been created by the cataclysmic eruptions. We rocketed upward, covering in several minutes a distance that had taken us months to traverse. And then suddenly we cleared the underworld, and shot out into the real world, right out the top of the Riemannn Roch Theorem.

As we clung to the lemma, it flew through the air, higher and higher before its trajectory peaked. Then we started earthward again, and I prayed for deliverance. As fate would have it, the lemma was wide enough to catch some air resistance, and we were lucky enough to land with a splash, unharmed, in the Algebraic Ocean, more than a thousand miles from where we had embarked on our adventure.

There we were picked up by some commutative algebraists who had been out trawling for lemmas. Within a short time, we found ourselves back at our home, hailed as the heroes who had reached the center of mathematics.

Of course, to this story there is an aftermath. Following such an adventure, it was difficult for each of us to adjust to the everyday world. The professor eventually gave up mathematics altogether. He spends most of his time now writing doggerel verse in runic and reading it to the chickens he keeps behind the house. Hansel dabbled with puppetry for a while, but eventually decided to go to mime school. And me, I have decided to become a logician. There was something special I felt at that instant when I understood how all of mathematics could come from nothing. And I just hope to capture that feeling again, even if only for a moment.

The Theorem Blaster

Is your theorem overweight? Need to trim the pages of your paper? Want to fit into that volume on semi-simple Lie Algebras? Then you're in luck! Because we are offering to the public for the first time ever, the amazing **Theorem Blaster**®. You've heard about it in the Math Lounge. You've seen it on Math TV. But now, due to a special purchase agreement with the American Mathematical Society, we can offer it to you at drastically reduced prices.

Overweight theorems can be dangerous in the long term. Sluggish and impenetrable, they cause colleagues to lose interest in your work, leading to publication-rate slowdown and severe career trajectory tailspin.

But now you can have the theorem you always dreamed of. Yes, if you want hot looking theorems, you want the **Theorem Blaster**®.

Here are just a few of the many testimonials from our satisfied customers:

"My proofs were ponderous and unwieldy. Many mathematicians refused to read them. But now I can't keep my preprints on the shelf. Colleagues can't keep their hands off them."—John Conrad, Princeton

"Little children teased me. 'You're hiding your lack of mathematical insight inside layers of impenetrable notation,' they chanted

in their barely discernable singsong voices as they played. I hated it, and I was intimidated, avoiding all contact with children. But now I walk past the playground with pride, my three-page preprint held up high for all the toddlers to see."—Robert Lazarus, Yale

"For many years, I could only submit to journals with no upper page limit, like the Transactions. Now I'm publishing two page notes in the Proceedings of the AMS. Thank you, **Theorem Blaster**®.*"*— Karen Hammond, Duke University

How does it work? By isolating the logical components of the core theorem and honing the fundamental connective tissue, the patented triple action technology of the **Theorem Blaster**® focuses its energies exactly where you need help the most. It burns off undesirable symbols and equations. It removes unsightly constants. It squeezes out the excess verbiage.

As a special bonus, the **Theorem Blaster**® comes with our special video "Five Days to Beautiful Proofs and Theorems." Watch as our Ph.D. trained personnel guide you in the use of your **Theorem Blaster**®. In five days, you can say with pride, "Hey, there, random person walking down the street! Take a look at this proof!"

Always lacked the confidence to show your proofs off at the Mathematical Sciences Research Institute in Berkeley? Afraid to take that long bus ride up the hill? In the pit of your stomach was the fear that seminar participants might point and laugh at the circuitous route you took to prove your theorem? Or even worse, *they might get up and leave in the middle of your talk*?

Well, live in fear no longer. Go ahead, get on the bus! Because they will be begging you for more theorems by the time you are done!

Well-known math trainer Steven Krantz has spent years teaching mathematicians to write clearly and concisely.

"I was amazed by the **Theorem Blaster**®, he said. "It's like liposuction for math. My book, 'A Primer of Mathematical Writing', is superfluous in the face of this amazing invention."

Do you have a closet filled with cumbersome machines, each bought on the promise of sudden size reduction? The Corollary Cutter, the Lemma Loser, the Conjecture Cruncher? Well, throw them all away. *You won't need them anymore!*

And what about Mathersize®? Or π-lades®? *All those reduction fads are out the window! That's right. You don't need them anymore!*

A top university released the results of a study demonstrating that the **Theorem Blaster**® is the fastest and safest method to reduce papers to a reasonable size. They compared it to other reduction methods and found that the theorem survival rate with the **Theorem Blaster**® approaches 95%, way outperforming the competitors.

And, believe it or not, as a special deal for those ordering today, in addition to the **Theorem Blaster**®, and the video "Five Days to Beautiful Proofs and Theorems," you will also receive instructions for the world-famous **Analysis Diet**®. That's right. The diet where you just drop analysis from your mathematical diet and watch the bloat come off.

Epsilons and deltas, gone! σ-algebras, gone! Radon-Nikodym derivatives, gone!

Your proofs will shrink at a dramatic rate. Watch as lemmas and corollaries are exposed to view for the first time. It will bring out definition, in fact, lots of definitions.

This opportunity is not available in any math department. Don't delay! Call our toll free number today. Why not order one for a friend as well? They will appreciate the help. We all will!

There is no guarantee that the bloat will stay off. Persons with heart conditions or difficulty digesting de Rham cohomology should consult their Ph.D. advisor before using the **Theorem Blaster**®.

Riot at the Calc Exam

There had been a lot of unrest in the classroom all semester. To a certain extent, I was to blame. I decided right at the beginning of the course not to waste any time. So the first day, I introduced the triple integral. It was quite a shock for students who had yet to see a single integral. But that's what I wanted. Shock therapy. Shock calculus. Embed an idea so deeply in their brains it would never get out. Brand their brains with a hot branding iron that said $\iiint$. Well, that first day, the smell of burning brain matter was overwhelming.

Slack-jawed students with bulging eyes gaped in disbelief and horror. Several flipped frantically through their class schedules to check if they were in the right room.

So I hit them with Fourier series to get their attention. By the end of that first day, they looked like the morning after an all-night dorm party called "Oktoberfest Meets Mardi Gras"—the bowed heads, the bloodshot eyes, the looks of nausea and anguish.

"It's no use sobbing," I told one woman as she left the classroom. "Either you can do it or you can't. Toughen up or get stomped all over."

Then she really started bawling.

But it's the truth. Knowledge isn't for the faint of heart. There is some nasty knowledge out there. You have to be able to take it. The citadel of learning isn't for the lily-livered.

By the next class at least half of the livers were gone. It was a big improvement. We were down to a much more workable group. Now I could practice the one-on-one intimidation at which I excelled.

We covered about 75 years of mathematics that day, from about 1837 to 1912. But I still wanted three more students to drop. Any more than that and I would fall below the eighteen-student minimum for the course to run.

So I gave them a pop quiz on complex analytic functors over quaternionic tangent bundles. At the end, thirteen students rushed up with drop slips for me to sign. I signed three.

The first few weeks of the semester, I didn't assign any homework. Why should I collect assignments that I had no intention of grading? It would just clutter up my office. But the students started to get nervous. Homework began to appear in my mailbox, problems from sections in the text that we were supposed to be covering.

It infuriated me, this unsolicited work. I would return it the next class, without having looked at it, only to find it in my mailbox again, several hours later.

So, finally, I was forced to assign and collect homework. I would slash over it with red magic markers and crayons at random. Then I would put big red F's at the top of each and write things like, "Have you considered a job at Seven Eleven?"

And so, we settled into the routine of the semester. Every few weeks, I would call the registrar and insist that the classroom was inadequate and had to be changed. It was a quick way to insure that the class was kept down to a reasonable size. I knew that those few students who really wanted to learn would find out where the class had gone. Optimal teaching conditions occur when the number of students per faculty is kept to the minimum possible. Logically, then, my goal was to lose them all.

But students in pursuit of passing grades are not easily shaken. Every time the class moved, students would show up. Usually though, the search for the new classroom made them late, and if there is one thing I will not abide, it is a lack of respect for time. At exactly 10:00, I would lock the door to the classroom. No matter how hard the late students banged on the door, whimpering and pleading, I wouldn't let them in. You have to learn discipline before you can learn mathematics.

There was one student named Wattle who was consistently late. He didn't even bother coming to the door. Each class meeting, at about 10:05, his head would appear at the window of whatever classroom we were in. He would stand outside and take notes for the entire hour. I considered having the class moved to the second floor, but after a while I became almost fond of that head bobbing outside the window.

As the semester progressed, students began to hound me. I could no longer go to my office during my office hours for fear of running into them. It got to where I would find them milling around my door at all hours of the day and night, wearing those sad hangdog looks, asking me where the class had moved and what were the assignments. The students, they just want to suck you dry.

About the eighth week, I lost control of the class. The balance of power in a classroom is always tenuous, and keeping the respect and awe of the students requires a delicate hand. I realized I had lost that control when they began to catch the blackboard erasers I hurled at them and fling them back. The student-teacher relationship was breaking down.

Things deteriorated quickly. When I strolled across campus, I was being hit by too many frisbees. Of course, anyone strolling across a college campus has to expect to be hit by one or two frisbees. It's part of being a pedestrian in a youth-encumbered environment. But I was averaging nearer to ten or twelve frisbees, a couple of footballs, and a baseball or two. Those baseballs can really sting.

One day, I was late to class. I had been debating the correct definition of the word "tangential" with a colleague and in my excitement, I lost track of the time. I arrived at the classroom at 10:05 and the door was locked. I could hear snickering from inside. That was when I decided I had had enough.

Wattle never saw me coming. I grabbed him in a headlock and said through the window, "Unlock it or Wattle arrives in hell earlier than expected." There was some debate, as Wattle was not particularly popular on campus, but they did open the door.

From then on, the students left me alone. They kept their distance. The few who continued to come to class usually sat in the back, and seemed inordinately skittish.

On the day of the final, I passed out the exam. I was pretty pleased with myself. Instead of having to make up two exams, one for the graduate course I was teaching and one for the calculus course, I just used the graduate exam for both. I know it sounds unfair, but there are a lot of constraints on a faculty member's time. One has to weigh all the responsibilities one has. In this case, making up the calc exam was outweighed by the Miley Cyrus special on T.V.

Unfortunately, Wattle noticed that the exam was for the graduate course. I had forgotten to change the course number in the upper right hand corner of the front page. He stood up.

"That's it. We don't have to take this anymore." He picked up the exam and crumpled it in his fist. A cheer went up.

"Sit down, Wattle. Sit down or you flunk," I yelled. He took the balled-up exam and hurled it at me. Suddenly all the students were up, screaming and yelling. Crumpled exams flew everywhere. A chair sailed across the room. I ran for the door.

When the police arrived, two students were wrapping the cord from the overhead projector around my neck. Quite frankly, I am lucky to be alive. I have only the student's penchant for alcohol and their resultant slowed motor skills to thank for my survival.

At the trial, I explained how the students, disgruntled with the downward spiral in their grades, had decided to take action. But rather than hitting the books and working diligently to improve their minds, they chose instead to murder the professor, and thereby prevent the distribution of grades. It was an unsuccessful attempt at cold-blooded premeditated first-degree murder. I was particularly eloquent. The judge sentenced them all to ten to twelve years at that educational facility, the Federal Penitentiary in Leavenworth, Kansas.

It was difficult for me to decide on the grades that they deserved. I considered petitioning the college to introduce a new grade, Z, which would essentially mean, "This student did so abysmally in the course that they deserve to die, but we did the next best thing. We had them locked away." In the end I gave them all F's except for Wattle. In a moment of weakness, I gave him a D-. I can imagine exactly how his head must look, bobbing behind the barred window at Leavenworth.

My next semester starts in a week. It is clear that I will have to run my classes more strictly this time. No more Mr. Nice Guy.

The Mathematical Ethicist

Dear Dr. Brad,

I have gotten in the habit of throwing a lavish banquet for my students the evening before I hand out the student course evaluations each semester. My question is whether or not it is appropriate to have the students fill out the forms at the banquet. There is a break in the festivities after the dinner but preceding the floor show which could serve for this purpose.

Best,

Waldo Wendt

University of Westport

Dear Waldo,

I am assuming that the course evaluations play a substantial role in the tenure process at your institution and further, that you are junior faculty. It is a rare senior faculty member who throws a banquet with floor show for his or her students.

Given these assumptions, it behooves you to behave in a manner that cannot possibly be interpreted to suggest, in the slightest way, that you are attempting to influence the outcome of the student course surveys. Even the hint of such impropriety could besmirch your career permanently. In other words, do not give the surveys out between dinner and the floor show. Wait until the next day. Besides, if they did fill them out right after the banquet, the students would not yet have experienced the floor show. So it could not influence their survey responses, a complete waste of what must be a major component of your budget. Common sense, fella?

-Dr. Brad

Dear Dr. Brad,

I was recently invited to give a talk at the prestigious Oberwolfach Tricentennial Conference on Number Theory. This was quite an honor for me, particularly since I am not a number theorist. However, when it was time for me to give my talk, the conference organizer introduced me by saying, "And here is the man who proved Fermat's Last Theorem, Andrew Wiles". Unfortunately, I am not Andrew Wiles, and it was at this point that I realized that a mistake had been made. It was never their intent to invite me at all. I looked out at the sea of expectant faces, and did the only thing I could do. I pretended to be Andrew Wiles for the next hour, receiving a standing ovation at the end. Did I do the right thing?

Andre Wilson

Prinsetown University

Dear Andre,

Under the circumstances, you did the right thing. You certainly wouldn't want to disappoint the audience, many of whom had come a long way to hear Dr. Wiles. Luckily, mathematics is esoteric enough that you can make terms up on the fly, and the audience members will be too embarrassed to acknowledge they have absolutely no idea what the heck you are talking about. So they applaud at the end, even though they haven't understood a word. Would you consider giving a talk at my institution? We can't afford Wiles.

-Dr. Brad

Dear Dr. Brad,

A paper of mine was recently published in the *Journal of Algebra*. It was a translation of a paper by an obscure Bulgarian author that appeared in 1972 in *Bioavtomatika*, the *Journal of the Bulgarian Academy of Science*. However, I did make a few changes in the spacing and in the numbering of the theorems. Unfortunately, the Bulgarian author discovered my translation (turns out he speaks English—who knew?) and he seems to be upset. Should I have referenced the paper in the bibliography?

Hortense Galbloddy
College of St. Geronimo

Dear Hortense,

Do ideas transcend the language in which they are stated? And is it the ideas with which we credit a creator? These are questions that I ask myself sometimes, when I am in the shower, and I don't feel like going to work. After several hours of consideration, I step out of the shower, a complete prune, and think about what to have for lunch. But enough about me and my day.

The short answer is yes, ideas do transcend the language in which they are created. Hence, if the ideas in your paper are exactly the same as the Bulgarian's ideas, you must credit him with their discovery. But what is an idea? How does one decide if two ideas are identical? These are questions I reserve for my time in the tub. My conclusion is that there is no idea yardstick which can be utilized to determine the size of an idea, and to compare it with the size of other ideas. So who is to say if your translation actually captures the same ideas that the Bulgarian was attempting to express? How can you know what was in his head? You can't. So sleep easy. You need not feel guilty for neglecting to include his paper in your references.

-Dr. Brad

P. S. Of course, the Ethics Committee at your institution may see it differently. You might want to send some expensive presents to your new Bulgarian friend.

Dear Dr. Brad,

At a recent conference, I saw a very nice talk on laminated deck transformations. Afterward, I suggested to the speaker that he might want to extend his results to polylaminated deck transformations. I was chagrined, six weeks later, when the editor of a prestigious journal asked me to referee a paper by this same speaker, in which he explained laminated deck transformations and the extension to polylaminated deck transformations, with no mention of me whatsoever. I see that I have three alternatives.

(1) I could contact the author and let him know I am the referee, making it clear there is no way I will recommend the paper for publication without my own name on it as co-author.

(2) I could submit my referee's report, recommend that the editor reject the paper, and in the mean time, write up my own version and submit it elsewhere.

(3) I could send out a blanket email to everyone in the field explaining how this cretin tried to steal my idea.

But whatever happens, I want to make sure that my actions are completely ethical and above reproach. I look forward to hearing from you as soon as possible.

> With great respect,
> Dr. Donald Dumpstead
> Ullalah U.

Dear Don,

The question of what constitutes a sufficient contribution to a paper to justify inclusion as a co-author is one of the most difficult and slippery in all of mathematics. It is a question that occupies my thought processes when I brush my teeth every morning. I reserve that time to consider it. Can a single lemma be enough? Brush, brush. One theorem, two theorems? Brush. And what about a corollary? Spit. Sometimes I find myself lost in thought, froth dribbling from my open mouth, the sound of banging on the bathroom door from desperate members of my family echoing in the background.

But in your case, the time it takes to floss should suffice. It boils down to a single word. Polylaminated.

In fact, your contribution wasn't even the whole word. It was actually just the prefix. Does a four-letter prefix justify inclusion as a co-author in a paper? It turns out that there is a precedent. In its landmark ruling of 1967, the Ethics Committee of the Canadian Mathematical Society determined that a prefix of three or fewer letters does not suffice to presume co-authorship. Hence the prefixes sub-, dis-, ir-, bi-, in-, co-, and non- do not cut the mustard.

However, in an intricate argument I will not attempt to recreate here, they determined that a prefix of four or more letters, *as long as at least one letter is from the last ten letters of the alphabet*, does suffice. Hence, any of para-, trans-, null-, pseudo-, semi-, ortho-, or quasi- will do nicely. But endo- doesn't quite make the cut. Of course, if the prefix contains a Greek letter, such as σ-, there is no lower limit on the number of letters necessary to warrant co-authorship. For God's sake, it's a Greek letter.

In your case, poly- does the trick. This means that any of the three alternatives you outlined above would be fully justified, and you can rest assured, if nowhere else, you will find support on the Ethics Committee of the Canadian Math Society.

-Dr. Brad

This concludes another column. But remember, when you find yourself tangled in the morass of mathematical morality, you are only an email away. I hope you don't have to write often. But a letter once in a while wouldn't hurt.

Conscientiously yours,

Dr. Brad Dearborn, Ph.D.

Phone Interview

John: Hello?

Dick: Yes, hello, is this John?

John: Yes, it is.

Dick: Hello, John, this is Dick Dermott calling back. I'm here with the hiring committee on the speaker phone. Let me introduce them.

John: Sure.

Dick: Seated to my right is Angela Ambertrout. She's a number theorist.

Angela: Hello, John.

John: Hi.

Dick: And to her right is Eric Enders. He is a logician. We like to kid him that for a logician, he is surprisingly illogical.

Eric: Ha, ha, yes, Dick's a kidder all right. Nice talking to you, John.

John: Hi.

Dick: And finally, last, but certainly not least, is Bob Klakity, sitting to my left. He was a geometer, but now, he's a muckety muck administrator. Isn't that right, Bob?

Bob: Ha, yes, I'm now the Dean of Arts and Sciences, but I check in with these jokers once in a while, just to make sure they haven't destroyed the department.

John: Nice to meet you.

Dick: And as you know, John, I'm chair of the department and my specialty is algebraic geometry. Of course, we are all familiar with your research, having read through the details of your file. But perhaps you could explain in more detail what you are working on to the committee. We're a diverse bunch, so please speak in monosyllable words only.

John: Ha, ha. Okay, sure. Well, I am interested in dihedral submonomorphoids defined over bilateral Bernoulli shifts. Although factorization theories for laterally subcutaneous rungs have existed since the early days of fibroid extensions, it is only in the last few years that lifts to hyperextended lower centralized series have allowed a complete classification of Alexandroff polyhedra in the category of ramified idempotents. . .

Eric: Hey, John, this is Eric. Sorry to interrupt, but are there any faces here?

John: Well, yes, the Alexandroff polyhedra have faces.

Eric: Can you lift them?

John: Well, yes, assuming that the fundamental group is locally extendable.

Eric: You know what that would be? A face lift. Get it? Oh, God, that's good.

John: Ummm, yes. That is funny.

Dick: Don't mind Eric, John. He's a bit of a joker. Please go on.

John: Yes, well, okay, as I was saying. It is only in the last few years that lifts to hyperextended lower centralized series. . .

Bob: Angela, didn't you hyperextend your thumb a couple years back?

Angela: Yes, Bob, I did. Hurt like a bitch. Had to wear a splint for a month.

Bob: Hey, John, maybe you should consider a splint for your hyperextended thingamajig. Is there a mathematical object called a splint?

John: Ummm. Not that I know of.

Bob: Well, we could make one up. Maybe we could do some joint work on that, publish a paper.

John: Ummm. Well, maybe. . . .

Eric: Bob wrote three papers with our last junior guy, what's-his-name, the one who didn't get tenure.

Dick: The skinny guy who always looked depressed? I can't remember. Started with an 'S', I think.

Bob: It was Shoemaker, or Shoestring or something about shoes. All I cared about was that it came after Klakity in the alphabet, hah hah.

Angela: Hey, John. I think we've heard enough about your research. Let's talk about your teaching.

John: Oh, okay.

Angela: Would you like to teach multivariable calculus?

John: Sure. I really enjoy that material.

Angela: Oops. Wrong answer, John. Eric has a lock on that course. Nobody teaches it but him.

Dick: Now, Angela, we talked about this. Nobody has a lock on any course.

Eric: Of course, I would be happy to let someone else teach the course. The minute you let me teach probability, Dick.

Dick: That's my course. I created it.

Eric: But I thought no one had a lock on a course.

Dick: It's different if there is only one person competent to teach it.

Angela: Just because you go to Las Vegas doesn't make you a probabilist.

Bob: Okay, gang, we don't want to give our candidate the wrong impression of our happy family. John, this is Bob again, the muckety muck administrator. I'm wondering what kind of supplies you need for your research.

John: You mean computer facilities?

Bob: God, no. I mean pens and pencils, paper clips, pads, and such.

John: Oh, ummmm, I need some of those.

Bob: Which ones?

John: All of them, I think.

Bob: Oh. Well, of course, if you absolutely need all of them, we could put in a request with the Start-Up Committee. But you might want to think about bringing whatever you need from your current institution. They won't miss it. We have a bit of a budget crunch here.

Angela: Bit of a budget crunch? Our department is housed in the basement of the Heating Plant. We haven't had a raise since South America shared a tectonic plate with Africa. The average class size has just past the centennial mark. Yes, we do have a bit of a budget crunch.

Dick: Angela, we are on the phone here. John, let's get back to talking about your teaching. According to your file, you have been quite successful in the classroom. Tell me this. What would you do if a student put you in a half-nelson?

John: What?

Dick: A half-nelson, you know where he has you from behind, with his arm hooked around your right arm and then back up behind your neck.

John: I, ummm, I have never thought about it. I hope I never find myself in that position.

Dick: Well, sure. We all hope that. But what would you do?

John: I would scream for security?

Eric: Oops, another wrong answer. Security doesn't have time to come running every time a faculty member finds himself in a half-nelson. You simply twist to the right, hooking your right leg through his legs. Then grab him at his belt with your left hand, pull hard and voila, he's flat on his back with you on top.

John: Oh. I see....

Dick: John, exactly how much teaching experience do you have?

John: I taught recitation sections throughout my graduate career. Calculus mostly. Then as a postdoc, I taught my own classes for two years.

Bob: Of course, the students you get there are quite different from our students.

John: In what sense?

Bob: They look different. They wear different clothes. They are sometimes shorter and sometimes taller than our students.

John: Umm, yes, but your students are sometimes taller or shorter than the students here.

Bob: Yes, now you seem to be getting it.

John: No, I don't think I am. How do the individual differences in height impact teaching?

Bob: All I am saying, young man, is that you have not taught our students. You have taught some other students. And the techniques that work on those other students may not work on our students.

John: Okay, you mean like your technique of how to get out of a half-nelson might not work as well here, since the student might be of a different height.

Bob: Are you patronizing me?

Dick: Um, John, I'm going to change the subject a bit. As you probably know, we are not allowed to ask you about your marital status.

John: Yes, I am aware of that.

Dick: Yes, so the only way we can find out about it is if you just tell us about it, without us asking.

John: Yes....

Dick: Right, so if you want us to be able to tell you about opportunities for a spouse, or a partner, you would need to fill us in on that spouse or partner, without us asking you for the information.

John: I see....

(Pause)

Angela: I don't think you do, John. Let's try something else. I give you an answer and you give me the corresponding question.

John: What?

Angela: Don't start yet. Wait until I give you the answer.

John: Ummm...

Angela: The answer is "I am married."

John: Ummm, the question is, "What is your marital status?"

Dick: That's right. Of course, we never asked it. You asked it.

John: Look, I'm not married, not that it is any of your business.

Dick: Oh, that is interesting unsolicited information.

Eric: Hey, I liked that game. Let's play more.

Angela: Okay. John, here is your next answer. Thirty-two students and a duck.

John: Excuse me?

Angela: I said thirty-two students and a duck.

John: And I'm supposed to come up with a question that has that as an answer?

Angela: Right. Go ahead. You have 15 seconds.

John: This is crazy. I don't know. What does this have to do with the job?

Angela: Time's up. The question was, "What is the enrollment in fluid mechanics?"

Bob: Good God, that's funny, Angela.

John: I don't know what to say.

Dick: No need to say anything. But answer me this. If you were a muppet, which muppet would you be?

John: Are you kidding?

Bob: It's not a hard question.

John: I don't see how this is relevant.

Eric: Just say Kermit. Then we'll believe you have leadership potential.

Angela: Don't give away the answers, Eric.

John: Doesn't anybody want to talk about my qualifications for the job?

Dick: No need, John. I think we have a good sense of what you have to offer. Do you have any questions for us?

John: Well, yes, I have one. Are you actually a pack of loony toons or do you just put on an amazingly accurate portrayal?

Dick: Hmmm, Bob, do you want to field that one?

Bob: My experience is that it's no portrayal. It's real as real can be.

Eric: Ha ha. That's good.

John: I think I am going to hang up now.

Dick: Wait. Don't hang up yet. I want to make you the job offer.

John: What?

Dick: Once in a while, a candidate comes along who impresses us so much, we don't need time to debate. In fact, during this entire conversation, the four of us have been signaling each other with a variety of nonverbal cues, cues that say, "Hire this guy."

Eric: That's right.

Angela: We would love to have you here.

Bob: I have seen some vigorous gesticulations in support of candidates over the years, but none as vigorous as what I have seen here today in support of you.

John: Are you kidding?

Dick: Hardly. And if you come, we'll teach you the secret hand signals. Eric did a shadow thing with his hands where he reenacted the entire scene of you struggling to escape a half-nelson. It was truly hysterical.

Eric: Oh, no. It wasn't any better than most of the other hand signals being flashed around here.

Dick: I will send along an official letter, and then we can get to the negotiations about the paperclips. Nice talking to you, John. You take care, now.

Angela: Bye, John.

Eric: So long.

Bob: We'll be in touch.

(Click)

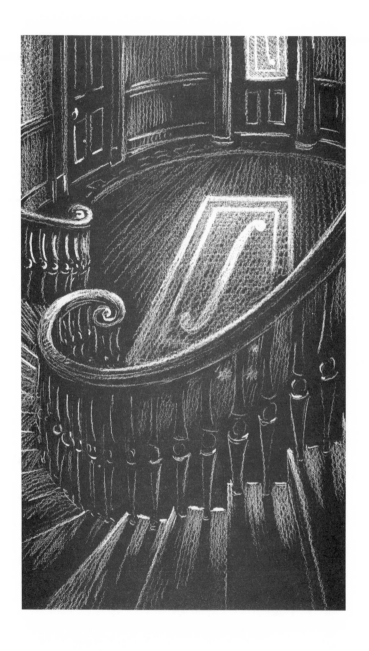

The Integral:
A Horror Story

Karen's eyes jerked open. She was soaked in sweat and the bedclothes were tangled around her legs. Her heart was beating at a fantastic rate.

She stared up into the darkness until she started to make out the bedroom. Slowly it dawned on her that it hadn't been real. It had been an awful dream. Philip touched her lightly on the arm.

"Another nightmare?" he asked.

She nodded. He pulled her to him and smoothed her damp hair.

"It's that house, isn't it?" he said. "Staying at that house with that guy Craig. That's what's causing the nightmares, isn't it?"

She nodded again. But she knew he misunderstood, that he thought the dreams were about the house. But the house didn't appear in the dreams. How could it? The dreams were the same dreams she had been having since she was 14 years old, for 20 years now, before she had ever heard of the house.

She closed her eyes, and the images from the dream immediately reappeared before her. She was standing alone on the dock, down by the lake where her family had spent their summers. But the sun didn't shine in the dream. There was no sun. Instead, everything around her was suffused with a dead gray light. A mist just three feet high crawled in over the water, slowly concealing the surface from view. She wanted to run. She needed to run. But her feet wouldn't move. It was as if they were fastened to the dock.

And then she heard it coming. The oars slipping into the water, creaking in their locks as the boat slid toward her. She wanted to cry out to her parents or her brother, but no sound escaped her throat.

And the boat emerged out of the fog, as it had in countless dreams before. The dark prow of the rowboat appeared first and then the back of the grey rain slicker, wet with moisture. As the craft approached the dock, the rower didn't slowed down. The boat rammed into the dock just two feet from where she stood. And then the lone passenger turned and smiled a sickening smile.

And even though, in her heart, she knew who it would be, she still felt the cold grip of fear as she gazed at Mr. Numskel, her 8th grade algebra teacher.

"Hello, Karen," he said, still grinning. She wanted to scream.

"If you can row your rowboat at 2 m.p.h. and run at 6 m.p.h., and you are 3 miles from a straight shoreline, and you must reach a point 8 miles down the shore as quickly as possible, for what point on the shore should you aim your craft?"

"I don't know, Mr. Numskel," said Karen, barely audibly.

"What did you say?" said Mr. Numskel. "Speak up, Karen. The class can't hear you." He motioned to the surrounding mist as he said it. Objects seemed to bob in the water just out of view.

"I don't know," she repeated.

"You don't know?" said Mr. Numskel, his voice rising. "We have drilled and drilled. We have worked on these problems for hours and hours. I have wasted so very much of my valuable time, and you say you don't know?" He was yelling now but still with that fixed grin.

He grabbed hold of the dock and pulled the boat to it.

Karen repeated frantically, "I don't know, Mr. Numskel. I'm sorry, but I don't know."

His grin had become even wider as he stood up in the bobbing boat and stepped onto the dock.

"There is an easy way to learn math, and a hard way," he said. "We tried the easy way with you, and it didn't work. Now we will do it the hard way." He reached for her throat. She screamed, and suddenly everything dissolved. She realized she was sitting up in bed and the morning sun was streaming in through the window.

In the beige tiled kitchen, Philip and Karen sat, mugs of coffee on the table before them.

"Why don't you call it off?" said Philip. "No one can make you go in that house tonight."

"Philip, you know I can't do that. We need the money. If I make it through one night, half the estate is ours. Then we will be able to get our internet site off the ground. But without the seed money, it's a nonstarter."

"I know," said Philip. "But I don't like it. It's too weird. You and that Craig Studdlehorn spending a whole night in that house."

"It's weird all right," said Karen. "But if you knew Numskel, you'd know it's in character."

"But why did Numskel pick you and this guy?"

"Oh, I know the answer to that. Craig Studdlehorn and I had Mr. Numskel the same year. Craig was the teacher's pet. One of those math genius types, always knew the correct answer. Never had to work at it. He and Numskel had a regular love fest. Numskel would ask someone a question, and then humiliate them when they couldn't answer. Then he'd turn to Craig, who always knew the solution. And more often than not, it was me Numskel was humiliating."

"And where's Studdlehorn now?"

"He got his Ph.D. in some area of abstract math called topography or something. As far as I can tell, he studies doughnuts and coffee cups. Or at least that's what he said when he buttonholed me at the ten-year reunion. Quite full of himself. Now he teaches at Central College, just down the road. Probably uses the same teaching techniques as Numskel."

"Okay, that explains Studdlehorn. But why were you included in the will?"

"I know the answer to that, too. It's Numskel reaching from beyond the grave to humiliate me one last time. He must have figured there's no way I would make it through the night. Then, Craig gets all the money and I get nothing. I had my chance and I blew it. I look like a loser one more time.

And that's the other reason why I have to go through with it. Because this time, that's not going to happen. For myself, I have to stick it out, and prove I can do it."

But even as she said it, she didn't believe it. She had been changed by Numskel's class. Before that, math had been easy. It just seemed obvious to her. But after that year with Numskel, math had always been a struggle. From that point on, she no longer trusted in her abilities. She always managed to convince herself she had it wrong. And even though she ultimately forced herself to take three semesters of calculus in college, it had been a living hell. The grades were passing but no more could be said for them. She picked English as a major, just to stay as far from math as possible. And since then, whenever anything remotely mathematical came up, she broke into a cold sweat.

Philip reached across the table and gripped her hand.

"We meet Studdlehorn and Evelyn Wachtel, the executor of the will, outside the house at 10:00 P.M. I'll be right outside the gates in the car with Wachtel all night. If anything happens, you and I both have cell phones. I can be there in two minutes." He gazed at her with a concerned look.

"Don't worry," she said. "Nothing will happen."

Watching him climb out of his Dodge Dart, Karen saw that Craig Studdlehorn looked almost unchanged since the last time she had seen him ten years before. He still wore his blonde hair in a crew cut, with penny loafers, white chinos, and red plaid shirt. The only changes were some new wrinkles around the eyes, a receding hairline, an expanding waistline, and a brown corduroy jacket with patches at

the elbows. He had had a prissy uptight cast to him in high school
and he still had it now.

"Ah, Karen," he said. "You look basically the same." He turned
to Philip. "And you are the loving hubby?"

"Yes, I'm Philip Casson, Karen's husband."

"I see," said Studdlehorn. He ignored Philip's proferred hand,
and turned to the executor. "Well, Ms. Wachtel, shall we get on with
it?"

"Yes," said the executor. "I believe everyone here understands
the rules. To receive half of the estate, each of you must remain in
the house until daybreak. No one else may enter. If either of you
fails to remain in the house, your portion of the estate is forfeited to
the other. If neither of you remains in the house, you both receive
nothing. Mr. Casson and I will wait out here in the car. Good luck."

She handed each a flashlight and motioned to the gate.

"After you," said Craig, as he moved aside for Karen. Philip
squeezed her hand and smiled reassuringly. Karen slung her bag over
her shoulder, turned on the flashlight and stepped through the gate.
Craig followed her through. The executor closed it behind them.

The two of them walked up the curving driveway together. Dried
leaves scuttled along the shadow-crossed asphalt.

"This is so weird," said Karen.

"Yes, it is strange, but don't worry, I'll watch out for you." Karen
stopped walking.

"What? You will watch out for me? That's just about the last
thing I expected you to say. Like you watched out for me in Mr.
Numskel's class? Is that the kind of watching out you had in mind?"

"Karen, if I teased you then, I apologize. I was 14 at the time.
That was many years ago. We have all matured."

"Well, maybe so," said Karen. She continued up the drive. The
house was still hidden from view.

"Where did Numskel get the money for all this?" asked Karen.
"He certainly didn't earn it on a teacher's salary."

"Oh, Mr. Numskel was quite clever," said Craig. "He devised an algorithm for investing in the stock market. It served him very well over the years."

The driveway curled around to the right. Suddenly the house loomed up before them. It was a massive Victorian built at the end of the 19th century, with a large porch wrapping around the front of the house. The shadows sliding over the darkened facade gave it a menacing appearance.

"Just like in the movies," said Craig with a laugh.

He motioned to the steps up to the front door. Karen looked up and her feet froze. Etched into the glass on the door was an integral sign.

Craig saw her reaction, and laughed. "It's okay Karen; it's just a symbol in the glass. Come on." He mounted the stairs, and inserted the key that Wachtel had given him. Twisting the doorknob, he swung open the door and shined his flashlight inside.

"All clear," he said, as he gestured for her to join him. She cautiously climbed the few steps, and edged through the front door. The house smelled musty. As her eyes adjusted to the darkness, she could see they were standing in a large tiled rotunda, with rooms opening to either side and a large stairway that rose as it curled up the round wall.

"Honey, I'm home," yelled Craig, and then he laughed. The echo of his laughter lasted a moment longer. He flicked the light switch on the wall but nothing happened.

"Wachtel said the power was turned off," said Karen.

"I know," said Craig peevishly, "but it doesn't hurt to try." He swept the rotunda with his flashlight. Various pieces of furniture were covered with sheets, most with enough dust to suggest the sheets were not a recent addition. On the far side of the room, Craig's flashlight passed over what appeared to be a large dark picture in a frame.

"Let's see what that is," said Craig as he strode across the rotunda, his heels echoing on the tile. Karen followed behind. As they approached, they saw it was a blackboard on a portable stand, leaning up against the wall.

"Look," said Craig, "there's something written on it. Number 1. Find the area of the triangle with vertices $(1, 2, 3)$, $(2, 4, -1)$, and $(3, 5 - 2)$." Karen felt dizzy. "Number 2. Determine the integral of $1/x$ when the limits of integration are 1 to ∞."

"Please stop," said Karen. Waves of nausea swept over her.

"There's only one more," continued Craig. "Find the volume of the intersection of two solid cylinders of radius r centered on the x and y axes respectively."

Karen reached to the wall for support. The room seemed to spin.

"Probably just some quiz he was working on for his students. You okay?"

"I think I need to lay down," said Karen weakly.

"Oh. Well, Wachtel said the bedrooms were upstairs. There are supposed to be fresh sheets on the beds and towels. Come on."

He took her arm and led her to the base of the stairs. They curled up into the darkness above.

"Think you can make it up? I'll help."

Together they slowly climbed the stairs, Karen leaning on Craig for support. As they climbed, Karen felt guilty for her assumptions about Craig. Maybe he really had changed, and he wasn't the same boy who had helped his teacher torment her so unmercifully all those years ago. The stairs creaked under their weight. At the top of the stairs, a long hallway stretched into darkness.

"I believe Wachtel said you should take the second door on the left and I'm the fifth door on the right."

Craig led her to her door. "Here you are," he said.

Karen looked at the door. "Um, Craig, would you mind coming in with me and checking out the room?"

"Sure," said Craig. "How often do I get invited into a pretty woman's bedroom?"

Something about his smile when he said this made Karen shudder. He turned the doorknob and pushed the door open.

Against the far wall was a canopied bed. The rest of the furniture was covered in sheets. But it appeared as if someone had dusted in here, and there were some towels folded at the base of the bed.

"Looks safe enough, I guess," said Craig. "Need me for anything else?" There was that queer smile again.

"No I think I'm all set."

"Okay, well, if you need me, remember, I'm the fifth door down on the right. Since you are the second door on the left, that would be $5 - 2 = 3$, isn't that right?"

Karen couldn't decide if he was taunting her, or if this was how Craig interacted with everyone.

"So you just exit your room and go three doors down if you need me. Otherwise, I'll see you bright and early in the morning, that is, unless you decide to sleep in." He laughed at his own joke, looked her up and down, and then left, shutting the door behind him.

Karen let out a sigh of relief, and went to lock the door, only to find there was no key to do so. She dropped her bag on the bed, and swept her flashlight over the room once more.

After checking under the bed just to be safe, she looked out the window. In the distance, she could just make out the blue hood of Philip's car peeking from behind a tree. It comforted her knowing he was almost in sight. She reached into her bag, pulled out the cell phone, and dialed his number.

"Hi, honey," she said.

"Are you okay?" said Philip, the tone of his voice betraying his concern.

"Yes, I'm okay. It's spooky here, but that's all."

"Remember, if you need me, you can call and I'll be there in two minutes. Okay?"

"Okay. Hey, I can see your car from my bedroom window. Can you come out by the hood and wave to me? It would make me feel a lot better."

"Sure, honey, just a sec."

She watched out the window for Philip to step by the car and wave, but he didn't appear.

Suddenly, down the hall, there was a huge crash. The noise startled Karen so badly, she dropped the cell phone. It hit the floor and broke into several pieces. She grabbed up the largest chunk. "Hello, Philip? Philip?" The phone was dead.

She stared at the door to her room, badly frightened, not knowing what to do. "Craig?" she called out timidly.

There was silence and then, a sudden knock at her door.

"Is that you Craig?" she asked fearfully.

"Of course it's me. Who else would it be?"

He opened the door. "Hope that noise didn't scare you."

"What was it?" asked Karen.

"Oh, I saw a piece of paper stuck behind the bureau in my room, and I was curious. Almost had it out, when I tipped the bureau a little too far and over it went."

"Oh, well, that's a relief. I have to admit, it gave me a scare."

"Did it? Well, you'll be interested. I got the piece of paper. Take a look."

He held it out to her as he shined the flashlight on it. It was a grade sheet. As she scrolled her eyes down the page, she realized she recognized the names listed there. It was the grade sheet from the math class she and Craig had taken with Mr. Numskel those many years past. Two of the names were underlined in red. Hers and Craig's. Craig's name was followed by an entire sequence of A's and 100's while hers was followed by D's and 60's. She shivered.

"Why would that grade sheet still be around after all these years? Craig, why did Numskel have this fascination with us? I mean he must have had hundreds of students over the years. What was so special about our class?"

"Oh, don't you know? Numskel's goal in life was to get out of the high-school teaching racket. He wanted to become an honest to God mathematician. He was taking night courses at Central College, intending to do a master's in math followed by a Ph.D."

"Yeah, so what?"

"So, the semester before we had him, he failed his prelims and got booted out of the program. That was the end of his dream."

"Really?"

"Yes, so when we came into his class, he was harboring tremendous resentment. Resentment he took out on you. And, I think he was living vicariously though me."

"I had no idea."

"Yes, well, it certainly doesn't excuse him, but it does help to explain him. At any rate, I'll let you get to bed now. That is, unless you would rather I stayed." Again the strange smile.

"No, I'll be fine. Goodnight Craig."

But he didn't turn to go. "I used to sit behind you in class."

"Yes, I guess you did."

"I used to look at the back of your head."

"Oh? I guess you would." Karen was getting more uncomfortable.

"Mostly, you wore a barrette at the back. It made a ponytail that went down your neck."

"Um, yes, so what's the point here?"

"I was in love with the back of your head."

"What?"

"Goodnight."

He stepped out the door and walked away down the corridor. She quickly shut the door, and wished desperately there were a lock. What the hell did he mean by that remark? He was in love with the back of her head? Did he mean he had had a crush on her, all those years ago? Could that be it? Could Craig Studdlehorn have been interested in her? But because he was socially inept, he teased her instead of letting her know how he felt.

Although it helped to explain his behavior those many years past, it disturbed her even more being alone in the house with him. She went over to the nearest piece of furniture and pulled off the sheet that covered it. It was a waist-high bookshelf filled with books. She gripped it near the top, and leaning into it, slid it across the floor until it blocked the door.

As she caught her breath, she noticed the books filling the bookshelf. All math books of some kind or another. Trigonometry, abstract algebra, complex analysis, algebraic topology. Half of them were terms she had never heard before. *Sheaf Theory, Linear Algebra, An Introduction to Number Theory.*

She couldn't help herself. With a hand that shook just slightly, she pulled the last off the shelf. It fell open to a page. She read, "**Theorem 2.7.** *There are an infinite number of primes.*" This was followed by the proof, which was so simple, even she could understand it. If there were a finite number of primes, then you could multiply them all together and add one to get a new number that was not divisible by any of the previous numbers. Hence, it would be a prime itself, contradicting the fact that you had listed all of them previously. It was so simple and so pretty.

She sat down on the bed with the book in hand and continued to read. She was shocked to discover how much of it she understood. And how much of it was beautiful. It was so concise, so logical, and so true. The statements built up on one another, one at a time, until you had a whole theory. She read about the distribution of primes and then about modular arithmetic and the theory of congruences. She was so engrossed that when she finally looked at her watch, she was surprised to see it was 1:00 A.M. She fished in her bag and pulled out the long t-shirt that she slept in. After changing, she climbed into bed with the book and continued to read. At some point she dozed off, book still in hand.

She was awakened by a small whirring noise nearby. When she opened her eyes, she was staring straight up at the bed's canopy above her. Two facts were immediately apparent to her. There was something written in embroidery on the canopy and the canopy was moving slowly down toward her on the bed.

"This must be a dream," she though to herself. She read the embroidery. It said "$\int \frac{dx}{1+x^2} =$?".

Her stomach began to churn. The canopy continued to move down toward her. If it didn't stop or if she didn't get out of the bed, she would be smothered. But nausea gripped her, and she found herself powerless to move. If only she could remember how to do that integral. It seemed vaguely familiar from her calculus class so many years before. It was like a trig function of some kind. The canopy ground slowly downward. And then it came to her. You could do it by a trig substitution, $x = \tan t$. Then you get the answer arctan x. That was it! "Arctan x," she screamed. But she found herself still unable to move. And the canopy was only a foot above her now. Then she remembered. "$+ C$, $+ C$," she screamed out and suddenly she could move again. She rolled out from under the canopy, falling to the floor just as the canopy closed over the bed.

She lay on the floor, breathing fast. With the realization of the need for the "$+ C$" at the end of the indefinite integral, all her nausea had disappeared.

She slowly rose to her feet. If she hadn't rolled out from under that canopy, she would have suffocated to death. Numskel was crazier than she thought. Suddenly she heard a scream from down the hall. Craig! She leaped to her feet and pushed the bookcase out from in front of the door. Grabbing the flashlight off the floor, she threw open the door. The hall was empty. She ran down to Craig's door, three down.

"Craig, Craig, are you all right?" she screamed.

She tried the door handle and found it unlocked. Throwing the door open, she saw Craig tied to the bed, face up, in pajamas covered in math symbols. He was sobbing as he looked straight up in terror. She followed his gaze to the ceiling, just in time to see a heavy blade drop from a hole. It missed him by a few feet and stuck point first into the floor. There were quite a few blades stuck in the floor, and several sticking up out of the mattress. At least one had drawn blood, staining the pillow by Craig's ear. Suddenly the bed itself spun around three times. Craig was stricken with fear. Then another knife dropped. It landed between Craig's spread legs on the bed. Craig shrieked.

Karen jerked one of the blades out of the floor, and was reaching over to free Craig's left hand, when suddenly the bed spun again, knocking her aside. She could see the circular crack in the floor surrounding the spinning platform on which the bed was mounted. As the bed came to a halt, Craig stared wide-eyed at the hole in the ceiling. Then he screamed as another blade dropped out of the hole. It pinned the side of his pajamas to the bed.

Karen jumped onto the bed, and cut the rope securing his left hand. The bed began to spin again. She leaned over Craig and cut his other hand loose. Then she leaped back and he sat up as a blade dropped right where his neck had been. She quickly cut lose his feet as the bed began to spin once more. They both threw themselves off the bed, crashing to the floor, as it came to a halt and another blade dropped where Craig had been lying.

Craig lay bawling on the floor, blood trickling down his neck. The bed had ceased its rotations. Karen stood slowly, still looking at the hole in the ceiling from which the blades no longer dropped.

"Come on, Craig. We have to get out of here," she said. But Craig continued to lay curled in a ball.

She grabbed him by his pajama top.

"Craig, get up. It's not safe in here. Get it together."

Trembling, Craig stood, and she pulled him out into the hall.

"Listen to me Craig. Numskel was crazier than we thought. He must have set this up. Installed machinery to kill us."

Craig was holding his ear.

"But I don't understand how you got tied to the bed. It wasn't a machine that did that."

"I don't know," moaned Craig. "I fell asleep and when I woke up I was tied to the bed. And then I saw the hole and... and... "

"Okay, Craig. Forget about that for now. We have to get out of here. Who knows what other booby traps are here?"

Karen and Craig ran down the hall and started down the stairs. Suddenly, when they were half way down, Karen grabbed Craig's arm.

"Stop," she screamed. She was looking at the base of the stairs.

"What?" said Craig. She pointed down to the bottom of the stairs where a large rectangular hole appeared in the floor.

"Oh, my God," said Craig. "That wasn't there last night."

"Come on, Craig. We can jump over it to the side."

There was a click, and the bottom stair disappeared. Karen's eyes widened. This was followed by a second click and the next stair retracted, leaving a shiny metal slide.

"Oh, my God, Craig," Karen screamed. "The stairs are retracting. This will turn into a slide and we'll go right into that hole. Quick, get up the stairs."

They both turned as they heard one click followed by another in quick succession. They threw themselves up the stairs two at a time, as the collapsing stairs approached. Just as they were almost at the top, the stairs collapsed beneath them, and the two of them slid down the curving ramp. Karen tried to reach over to the banister to catch hold, but Craig was in her way. With a sickening feeling, she felt herself leave the end of the ramp and fly into the hole in the floor. She landed with a thud on the floor below. Craig landed next to her.

She was bruised, but otherwise all right.

"You okay?" she asked. Craig looked confused.

"No. Where are we?"

"I don't know," Karen replied. "Must be somewhere in the basement of the house." She felt along the floor until she found her flashlight and then she shined it about them. They were in an open-topped box, about 12 feet by 12 feet with a height of 8 feet. The walls appeared to be made of iron, with large bolts securing one section of wall to another. There were no openings of any kind other than the hole through which they had fallen.

"It's almost like a tank of some kind," said Karen.

Over on one wall was a nozzle and some kind of machinery with an LED display. Karen and Craig walked over to it.

"What is that?" asked Craig

Suddenly, the display lit up with the number 1, and water started to squirt from the nozzle. They both jumped back.

After a minute, the water stopped squirting. Then, the display switched to 1/2 and the water squirted out again. Only half as long. As they watched open mouthed, the display subsequently showed 1/3, 1/4, and 1/5, each time squirting water for that fraction of the initial time. A puddle of water spread across the iron floor.

"Oh, no," Craig wailed. "We are going to be drowned. We are going to die."

"What are you talking about?" asked Karen.

"Don't you see? It's the harmonic series."

"What's the harmonic series?"

"The water that's coming in. It's being squirted in increments corresponding to the terms of the harmonic series. First was a gallon, then a half gallon, then a third of a gallon. Keep going and that adds up to the harmonic series."

"So?"

"So, the harmonic series diverges. Do you know what that means? Eventually, this room will fill with water. It doesn't matter how big the room is. Eventually it will overflow. And you and I will be dead. Do you see what I am saying? We will be dead!"

Craig, I'm not so worried."

"What's wrong with you? Don't you get it? The math isn't complicated. $1 + 1/2 + 1/3 + 1/4 + \cdots$ equals infinity!"

"But Craig, there is at least a five-second break between the times it squirts each portion."

"So?"

"So that means that over the next, say, six hours, there will be less than 12 times 60 times 6 portions emptied into the room. That means we sum up the first 4320 terms of the harmonic series."

"Oh, my God," said Craig. "How much is that?"

"Well, can't we approximate it with the integral from 1 to 4320 of $1/x$?"

"Yes, that sounds right."

"That is the natural log of 4320. It's about eight and a half gallons of water."

"What?" said Craig.

The spigot continued to spurt small amounts of water into the room. Craig stood up.

"We're not going to drown?"

"Not in this century. Come here, Craig. Give me a boost up. I think I can reach the edge."

"But, then you might leave me here."

"Relax, Craig. I won't leave you. We're in this together. Clasp your hands together."

Craig did so and Karen stepped up onto his hands and reached up to grasp the edge of the tank. She then stepped onto Craig's shoulder and pulled herself over the edge.

Standing up, she glanced around the rotunda. Spotting a sheet covering a chair, she brought the sheet over to the hole, tied part of it around the bottom of the bannister, and dropped the rest over the side.

"I can't pull myself up," moaned Craig.

"Hang on," said Karen. She slid the chair over to the edge of the hole.

"Stand back," she warned, and then she pushed the chair over the edge. It banged down hard on the metal floor. Craig set it back on its legs, and standing on it, he managed to hoist himself out of the hole. The water continued to spray out of the spigot.

"Stupid trap," said Craig, as he sat on the floor, catching his breath.

"Yes, it wasn't much of a trap," said Karen thoughtfully. "Numskel was smarter than that."

Craig stood carefully.

"I want out," he said. He started toward the front door when a loud click made him freeze. A sequence of waist-high equally spaced holes had suddenly opened in the rotunda walls.

"What the hell?" said Craig.

"Craig, get down," cried Karen, as she dove for the floor. There was another click and a crossbow arrow shot out of one of the holes, whizzing by Craig's shoulder and embedding itself in the far wall with a thunk. Craig stood paralyzed, unable to grasp what was happening. Karen crawled over to where he stood, grabbed him around the knees and tackled him to the floor just as another arrow shot out of one of the holes and whizzed over their heads.

Karen quickly surveyed the room.

"Craig, it looks like there are 17 holes, and two arrows have fired. So there are 15 to go. We have to get out of here."

"It's the heptadecagon," mumbled Craig.

"The heptawhat?" asked Karen.

"The heptadecagon, a 17-sided regular polygon. Karl Gauss proved that you could construct one just using a compass and a straightedge. He showed it when he was just 19."

"So?"

"So, it was a big deal in 1796." There was a click and another arrow shot out of one of the holes in the wall. It brushed by Craig's head as it flew over. He shrieked and flattened himself on the floor.

"Craig, they are shooting lower. They seem to be adjusting to where we are in the room. Quick, crawl after me toward that door."

Karen began to slither her way toward the nearest door. Whimpering, Craig followed. As she reached up for the door handle, there was a click and an arrow shot across the room, embedding itself quivering into the door less than an inch from her arm. She quickly turned the handle, threw open the door and rolled through. Craig crawled after her. She swung the door closed, just as she heard another click followed by another thunk in the door.

They lay in total darkness, breathing heavily.

"Craig, you okay?" asked Karen.

"I want to go home," whispered Craig back.

"Come on," said Karen. "Let's get moving."

"But I can't see anything."

"You want me to reopen the door?"

Craig fell silent.

Karen felt along the floor until she came to a wall. Then she carefully stood up.

"Follow my voice to the wall," she said.

"Okay, I'm at the wall," said Craig.

"Give me your hand. Okay, now we feel along the wall."

Karen slowly moved down the hall, keeping one hand on the wall, as Craig followed behind, holding her other hand. She could feel him trembling.

"Here's a doorway," she said. She tried the handle but it was locked.

"Let's keep going, Craig."

As she felt her way past the doorway, the door suddenly swung open, spilling light into the hall. Craig broke free of her hand and shrieked, falling against the far wall. As the door finished swinging open, Karen shrieked herself.

For there before them stood Numskel. He had that same sick grin he had had in her dream. She stared open mouthed. He turned to look at her, and she noticed a long knife in his hand.

"You're dead," she screamed. His smile broadened. Then he stepped across the hall and with one hand, lifted Craig by the front of his pajamas.

"How do you find the volume of a solid?" asked Numskel, almost whispering. He held the knife to Craig's throat. Craig whimpered.

"This can't be happening," said Karen.

"You know what Karen? I don't have all day," said Numskel "HOW DO YOU FIND THE VOLUME OF A SOLID?" He dug the point of the knife into the skin at Craig's throat.

"You measure it. Length times width times height," said Karen.

"Really?" said Numskel. "Length times width times height? So if I took Craig's height, say six feet, times his width, looks to be about a foot, times his length, also about a foot, I get six cubic feet for Craig's volume. Is that right?"

"No..."

"He would have to be a rectangular solid to get the right volume that way. So how do we find the volume of an irregularly shaped solid like Craigy boy here?"

"I don't know."

"What about this idea? What if we approximate Craig by a collection of rectangular boxes? See, we cut Craig up into little pieces. Each one is a tall slender box-like solid with a tiny rectangular base. But the top isn't right, since Craig is not flat on the top. But that's okay, because its volume is close to being given by its length times its width times its height. Add up the volume of all of the boxes and we get Craig's volume, at least approximately. The more boxes we use, the better the approximation. Shall we try it?"

"No, I think I get the idea. You don't need to demonstrate."

"Oh, but Karen, I think I do need to demonstrate. I need to very badly. First we do a rough approximation, say cut him into four pieces, and then we cut him up finer and finer."

Craig whimpered helplessly as Numskel moved the knife to his midsection.

"Wait, Mr. Numskel," said Karen. "I have a question."

"Yes, what is it?"

"You are taking a limit when the number of boxes goes to infinity. How do you know it converges?"

"What?" said Numskel.

"How do you know the sum of volumes approaches a particular number?"

Karen slowly moved toward Numskel.

"Of course it converges," he replied. "We cut Craig up into lots of little pieces. Each one has a volume that is approximated by the volume of a rectangular box. Each one has a volume that we can calculate. And if we use enough of them, we will get a better and better approximation of the actual volume."

She continued to move closer.

"But what are the restrictions on the function that defines Craig in order to make sure it converges?"

Numskel looked lost in thought for a second as he considered the question.

"Does it need to be differentiable, or continuous? What are the restrictions on its domain?"

As Numskel contemplated the question, Karen took another step forward and punched him in the nose with all her might. For a ghost, his nose made a satisfying crunch, as his head snapped back and he crumpled to the floor.

She looked down at his still form.

"Craig, take off your pajama top. We can tie him up with it." Surprisingly, Craig did as he was told. Karen flipped Numskel onto his back and pulled his arms together. Then she wrapped the pajama shirt around his wrists and tied the sleeves tightly together. Numskel's eyes suddenly regained their focus. He struggled for an instant and then looked up at Karen. Blood trickled from his nostril.

"Perhaps I underestimated you," he said.

"Perhaps you always underestimated me," replied Karen. "Now how about explaining how it is that you are here instead of buried under the ground?"

"You don't understand, do you Karen? Shall I have Craig explain it to you?"

"I don't understand either, Mr. Numskel," said Craig plaintively.

"Craig, you have been a major disappointment to me. You were to be my heir, to follow in my footsteps. To spread math anxiety."

"I can do that," said Craig.

"To do that, you need two things. One is knowledge of mathematics. Given your Ph.D. I thought you would do better in that category. The other is an innate sense of your own superiority. You have to believe in your heart that you know more than anyone else to truly intimidate them. You are lacking in that category, Craig."

"But how are you alive?" interrupted Karen. "You had a heart attack. They pronounced you dead."

He laughed. "Life and death are such discrete concepts. Like good and bad. . . like black and white. But the universe isn't discrete."

"What do you mean?" said Craig. "Of course life and death are discrete. Either you're alive or you're dead. There's no in between."

"You think you know so much, but you know so little," said Numskel. "That has always been your problem, Craig."

"There are so very many states of existence. People treat life and death as if they correspond to the numbers 0 and 1. Either you are alive or you are dead, a binary choice. But what about all the numbers between 0 and 1? There is a continuum of possibilities, infinitely many of them, uncountably many of them, states that lie between the two you know of as life and death. And that is just the states that correspond to the real numbers. What about the complex numbers? What about the quaternions?"

Karen felt anxiety rising in her chest. And as she became more uncomfortable, she could see Numskel's strength returning.

"We are dealing here with a power greater than death," he said.

"There is nothing greater than death," said Craig.

Numskel laughed again.

"Math anxiety is stronger than death. You may not realize that Craig, but I bet Karen does. It is one of the greatest forces on the planet. And it can be harnessed."

"You are not only dead, you're crazy, too."

"Am I, Craig? Then explain to me how I am here. I was dead and buried. And I dug my way out with my bare hands. I came back. Why? Because the power of math anxiety courses through my veins."

"Are you saying that math anxiety is a force? A force that re-animated you?" asked Karen incredulously.

Numskel turned his head to look at her as his nasty smile spread across his face.

"It animated me in life and death. Do you not see the power of it? I first felt that power many years ago. What was I then? A pathetic math teacher, socially inept, incapable of a meaningful relationship. In the real world, I would have been a laughingstock incapable of holding down a job."

"But in the classroom, I could use mathematics to intimidate students. I could shame them. And in so doing, I felt better about myself."

"The selfsame reason bullies have always bullied," said Karen.

"Yes, but this was a bit different, my dear. Because as time went on, I began to see changes in myself. The more I intimidated the students, the stronger I became. I was drawing power directly from the math anxiety I was creating around me. Do you know what it feels like to give an impossible exam to 25 eighth graders? Do you know what it feels like as the entire classroom fills with fear? I fed off that fear, from generation after generation of students."

"But you died," said Craig. "Power or no power, you died."

"Yes, I died. I had twice the strength of a normal person. But my heart couldn't handle the increased load. And I might have stayed dead, but I was a bit lucky there. A case of a gravedigger who had miscalculated the number of bodies that he was supposed to have buried. The proximity of his anxiety was enough to bring me back to life. And now I have come back from the grave for more."

"Do you know the square root of 3,481 Craig? Karen, what's the greatest common divisor of 76 and 164? These simple questions are enough to cause you anxiety. And your anxiety feeds my power."

"You can't make me feel anxious," said Craig. "I have a math Ph.D. I have a higher degree than you ever attained. Nothing you say could make me anxious."

"Is that so, Craig? Shall we talk about your thesis then?"

"What about my thesis?"

"Shall we talk about Lemma 3.7.2?"

Craig's mouth dropped open.

"Allow me to quote: *If H is a tangent horoball in the cusp diagram of a hyperbolic knot complement, then it corresponds to a maximal cusp.*"

Only there is a little problem there, isn't there Craiger? A little problem that you didn't discover until a week before your defense. And you never did find a fix for that problem, did you? Instead, you just covered it up, and hoped no one would look too closely at that lemma, one of fifty lemmas in your thesis. And nobody did notice the problem, did they? But you're not the expert on hyperbolic 3-manifolds that you pretend to be. In fact, your degree is a fraud."

"I will fix it one of these days," said Craig desperately. "It's such a small thing. Everything else in the thesis is correct. It's not fair that it all be wrong because of one tiny mistake." Craig looked as if he might burst into tears.

"But you're not going to fix it, Craig. You can't. Because you see it is wrong."

Craig turned white. He was shaking all over. Numskel visibly drew strength from Craig's anxiety. Veins stood out in his forehead. His face took on a red glow. Suddenly, he leapt to his feet and began to strain against his bonds. There was a ripping sound.

"Quick, Craig, come on," screamed Karen as she dragged him back down the hall to the door through which they had entered. Numskel threw off the torn pajama shirt that had held him, scooped up the knife, and bounded down the hall after them.

"But the arrows," said Craig, as they reached the door. Karen threw it open and pushed him through. He shrieked as he heard the mechanisms in the walls homing in on his position. Karen threw her shoulder into him, knocking him to the ground. As Numskel followed them through the door, reaching for Karen, the first arrow thunked out of its hole and caught him mid chest, nailing him back against the doorframe. He thrashed furiously, trying to pull himself free. A second arrow bolted out of the far wall and pinned his arm to the wall, as the knife clattered to the floor. Ten more arrows thunked into various parts of his body, one after the other, until it was clear there were no more arrows to launch.

"He's still alive," said Craig incredulously.

Numskel slowly turned his eyes on Karen, as blood dripped from his multiple wounds.

"What is the arc sine of square root of three over two?" he uttered with difficulty.

She stood up slowly.

"Hmmm...., interesting question. As I remember it, a 30-60-90 triangle has edge lengths 1, $\sqrt{3}$, and hypotenuse of length 2. Since $\sqrt{3}$ is the larger of 1 and $\sqrt{3}$, that means that the 60 degree angle must be the one opposite the $\sqrt{3}$ edge. So, then the sine of 60 degrees is $\sqrt{3}/2$. And therefore, the arc sine of $\sqrt{3}/2$ is 60 degrees."

Blood bubbled up out of Numskel's mouth.

"You can't know that," he said.

"Or $\pi/3$, if you prefer your answer in radians," she added.

Numskel tried to speak but only blood dripped out of his mouth. Then his head dropped down onto his chest and he was still.

"Is he dead?" asked Craig, as he cautiously rose up off the floor.

"According to what he said, there are so many possible states of existence, it's hard to know that he is categorically dead. But at the very least, he's within epsilon of death, even if he isn't dead in the sense we think of it."

"But how do we stop him from coming back to life?"

"Well, if we can convince the executor that he needs to be cremated, and then we spread the ashes far and wide, I'm hoping that will do the trick."

"How did you know the answer to his question?" asked Craig.

"You know, it's funny, but I always liked trig. Triangles never scared me. C'mon, Craig. It looks like it's morning. Let's get out of here."

She stepped across the rotunda to the front door, and turned the handle. The door swung open.

"But are we safe now?" asked Craig. "How do we know math anxiety won't rise up again, to take over other math teachers... teachers like me?"

"There will always be math anxiety," replied Karen. "And its power will always have an attraction to teachers. But if we can make people aware of its dangers, perhaps we can prevent this from ever happening again. Perhaps we can arm students to fight it. And we can caution teachers about its seductive powers."

"How do we do that?"

"I was planning to create a website about math anxiety, a place where students could go for help. Now, I know how important that is."

"Can I help?" asked Craig.

"Of course you can," said Karen. "I would appreciate the help."

They stepped out onto the porch. Karen turned, grabbed the handle and slammed the door hard. The door's large glass pane shattered, sending small shards of glass containing pieces of the etched integral symbol crashing to the porch.

"Oops," she said, smiling.

The Three Little Pigs

Once upon a time there were three little pigs who lived with their mother, a mathematician at Nebraska. The first little pig adored number theory. His goal in life was to prove the Swine-erton–Dyer Conjecture. The second little pig was fascinated by questions about complexity. Her goal in life was to prove that Pig = NPig. The third little pig loved algebraic geometry. He wanted nothing more than to prove the Hog Conjecture.

One day, their mother said, "I have taught you everything I know. It is now time for you to go to graduate school." So each pig packed a small bag filled with their favorite math books, slung it on a stick and set off to make their way in the mathematical world.

The first little pig earned a Ph.D. at the University of Illinois and obtained a post doc at Columbia. In his first year there, he announced a proof of the Swine-erton–Dyer Conjecture. Hugo C. Wolfe was visiting Columbia from Berkeley at the time, and after devouring the preprint, he rushed down the hall and banged on the little pig's door.

"Little pig, little pig," he roared. "It is I, Hugo Wolfe, from Berkeley. Open the door and let me in."

The little pig, who had recently grown a fashionable goatee, replied "Not by the hair on my chinny chin chin," as he cowered inside his office. For he was afraid of Hugo C. Wolfe, as was everybody else in mathematics.

"Then I will huff and puff and find a hole in your proof." And Wolfe huffed and he puffed and he came up with a hole in the first lemma.

"But there can't be a hole in the first lemma," squealed the little pig. That is a folk lemma that has been around forever."

Wolfe laughed viciously. "You should know better than to rely on a folk lemma." And the little pig's proof fell apart like a house made of straw, and the little pig's career did likewise.

The second little pig earned her Ph.D. at Wisconsin and she received a post doc at Rice University. In her second year there, she announced a proof that Pig = NPig. After reading the preprint posted on the web, Hugo C. Wolfe immediately flew to Houston and arrived at the little pig's office door.

"Little pig, little pig, it is I, Hugo C. Wolfe," cried Wolfe in his most intimidating manner. "Open the door and let me in."

"Not by the hair on my chinny chin chin," replied the second pig. Although she didn't have any hair on her chin, her brother, who now worked in kitchen supplies, had told her it was tradition to say this.

"Then I will huff and puff and find a hole in your argument."

And Wolfe huffed and he puffed and he found a hole in the second lemma.

"That lemma can't be wrong," said the second pig through the door. "I found it on the web. I'll fix the proof." But the hole could not be fixed, and her entire proof came tumbling down like a house made of sticks and the second little pig's mathematical career did likewise. Discouraged, she opened a barbecue joint in South Houston, revelling in the irony of it all.

The third little pig received his Ph.D at Northwestern University, and took a post doc at Michigan. After three years of work, the little pig announced a proof of the Hog Conjecture.

Hugo C. Wolfe didn't even wait to read the preprint. He rushed to Michigan, relishing the opportunity to destroy the third pig's career as well.

"Little pig, little pig, open the door and let me in."

"I go by Herbert T. Boar," replied the pig through his closed door.

"Open the door, Boar, or I will huff and puff and create a counterexample that will destroy this entire department."

"Listen, Wolfe, I'm not scared of you. I know my proof is airtight. The lemmas are all from refereed journals and I checked each one of their proofs myself. So huff and puff away."

Now Wolfe was greatly angered that the pig wasn't afraid of him. So he huffed and he puffed, but no counterexample came to him. So he huffed and puffed some more. He tried to show that the tangent bundle did not lift to the universal cover. He attempted to prove that the metric was not, in fact, Riemannian, but still to no avail. Finally, he banged on the pig's door once more.

"Little pig, little pig," he roared. "I don't have a counterexample yet, but it's only a matter of time."

The little pig said, "I'm not afraid of you. Even the weakest link in my argument, that Dehn filling the cusped 3-manifold yields a hyperbolic orbifold is safe from you."

Wolfe stood outside the door and stroked his long nose, a malevolent smile creasing his face. Then he stalked off down the corridor.

The little pig was awarded The Fields Medal, the award to be given at the International Congress of Mathematics, taking place in Porkugal. Before the ceremony, each of the awardees was to give a talk. As the little pig finished his remarks, the master of ceremonies opened the floor to questions. Hugo C. Wolfe stood up. "Little Pig," he said. "I have a question." A hush fell over the audience, for they knew what it meant when Hugo C. Wolfe had a question.

"It appears to me that in Lemma 3.4, you Dehn fill the Whitehead link complement to obtain a hyperbolic orbifold. But the result is not in fact an orbifold at all. It is a manifold." Wolfe grinned wickedly.

The little pig smiled back confidently. For Hugo C. Wolfe had fallen into his trap.

"Yes," said the pig, "but as any graduate student knows, a manifold is an orbifold, just with trivial singular set."

Wolfe began to turn red. "Well, yes, I suppose that is true," he mumbled. He began to sweat. It suddenly felt much too hot in the room. "But anyway," he added, "You don't know that the isometry group will have a subgroup of order p." He was grasping at straws now, but he was desperate. Everyone was looking at him, some smiling.

"As any undergraduate mathematics major can tell you," replied the pig, "the Sylow subgroup theorems imply that since p divides the order of the isometry group, there must be a subgroup of order p."

Wolfe's collar felt much too tight. He found he couldn't swallow. He felt like he was on fire. Someone laughed. Suddenly everyone was laughing. Wolfe tried to disappear, to sink beneath the chairs around him, but there was no escape. Everyone was laughing and pointing. Wolfe let out a strangled cry and ran out of the auditorium, never to be seen in mathematical circles again.

Eventually, the little pig became chair of the department at Michigan, which was housed in a beautiful brick building designed by the pig himself. He invited his brother and sister to come live with him in Ann Arbor, where they created the first dinner theater serving up hickory smoked barbecue with lectures on projective algebraic varieties. And the dinner choices were chicken, beef, and soy meat substitute.

Northnorthwestern State University Mathematics Department Safety Manual

Welcome to Northnorthwestern State University (NNWSU). We here at the Office of Office Safety(OOS) are happy to be one of the first offices on campus to welcome you to the Department of Mathematics. As a new member of the faculty, this document is one of a pile of documents that you have just received. ***BUT IT IS THE MOST IMPORTANT!*** Because safety is our number one concern here at NNWSU. You might have thought it was education, or research, or bringing in grant dollars, or showing support for our surprisingly large football team. But, no, it is safety.

Of course, new faculty members might not associate safety issues with a mathematics department. They might think that safety concerns should be relegated to chemistry departments, where an exploding beaker can send shards of glass streaking toward an unprotected eyeball, or physics departments, where an errant laser can burn holes in the seats of pants and what they contain. These new teachers may believe that they need not fear for their physical safety when working in a mathematics environment. But some of these new faculty are no longer employed at Northnorthwestern. In fact, some of them are not employed anywhere, because *they no longer walk this earth!* **So please read this document carefully.** *It could save your life!*

1. *What is the number one safety concern in a mathematics department?*

This is an *excellent* question. We made it up, but it is an excellent question nonetheless. The number one safety concern is eyestrain. Did you know that? I bet you didn't. Strained eyes cause more lost workdays than any other single mathematics office injury. Often, we see faculty members driving erratically, on their way home after a debilitating eyestrain injury. Often, they are pulled over by police who believe they are intoxicated, and who ask them to walk a straight line. And often they fail, because of eyestrain. Then it's off to the pokey for them. *Don't let this happen to you!*

2. *How do eyestrain injuries occur?*

Another excellent question. And yes, again, we made it up.

There are three main categories of eyestrain injury.

(A) **Eye Fatigue Syndrome (EFS):** Just as we can strain a leg muscle from overexertion, we can strain our eyes by staring in one direction too long, say at a computer screen or at a particularly enchanting fractal poster.

What can be done to prevent or alleviate EFS? Here are some **Eyestrain Prevention Exercises (ESPE):**

(i) Look away from the computer screen, say out your office door. Cup the palms of your hands over your eyes and stare out for 60 seconds, counting out loud. Then slowly twist your wrists to alternately cup your eyes and create blinders while staring out your door at anyone looking in. Continue for 60 seconds. Then cup with one hand while making a blinder with the other. Alternate hands back and forth for another minute.

(ii) Close one eye. Moving the opposite hand in a clockwise circle of diameter one foot, follow the index finger with the open eye. Do this for three revolutions and then change eyes. If anyone is staring at you through your open door, look from their feet up to their head and then back down to their feet six times. Then return to work.

(B) **Sudden Eye Movement Injury (SEMI):** This injury occurs when you are in your office working at your computer and a student comes to the open door. "Excuse me professor, but I don't think I should have lost this point on the homework." You suddenly jerk your eyes from the screen to the doorway and feel an immediate explosion of pain caused by tearing the muscles that control eyeball direction.

What can be done to prevent SEMI?

(1) Keep the office door closed.

(2) When there is a knock at the door, do not swivel the eyes quickly to the door, but rather, move them slowly toward the door, taking time to peruse the items you see along the way. Avoid jerky eye movements at all times.

(C) **Repetitive Eye Roll Injury (RERI):** This injury typically occurs at department meetings. Excessive rolling of the eyes can cause severe fatigue of the muscles under the upper eyelid, and leave one incapable of looking anywhere but down without pain. The common misconception that mathematicians are shy is a direct result of this phenomenon. If, however, you are a representative of the faculty senate, you have had ample opportunity to condition your eyes to rolling. So *roll on*!

3. Is it safer to work with a pencil or a pen?

Here at Double-North-West, pen injuries exceed pencil injuries by six to one. **Yes, six to one!** We have had three pen injuries and about half a pencil injury. How to explain the discrepancy? We don't know, but there it is. You choose pen and you may be writing your own obituary.

4. Must I wear loose-fitting clothes?

Yes, you *must*. Constricting clothing can be a constant distraction, causing you to lose focus on safety issues, and risk calamity. But not so loose that they fall off, causing a distraction for your fellow workers as they are handling sharp implements.

5. *What is the most dangerous object in a mathematics department?*

Great, great question. This is an easy one, too. It is the cups of coffee. Many people have claimed that styrofoam cups were the greatest invention in history. We here at the Double-N-Double-U-SU-Double-O-S beg to differ. The styrofoam cup is perhaps the most dangerous invention ever, as measured by the Steiner Hot Coffee Burn Index. They are tippy and they retain the heat in the coffee. This is an obvious recipe for disaster. More members of the Mathematics Department have been treated for coffee burns than for any other single kind of burn, with the exception of rug burns, which really don't deserve to be called burns at all.

We actually keep spare pairs of pants at the OOS for members of the Mathematics Department who spill coffee on themselves. We have men's cuffed tan pleated slacks, in a size 34 waist, and women's gabardine plaid slacks in a size 6, in case you want to plan ahead. Well, actually, we don't have the men's slacks right now. We are waiting to get them back from a certain someone who we suspect is purposely spilling coffee on himself just to get to use the slacks.

6. *Why is mathematics so dangerous?*

You have to understand. Mathematics is perhaps the most abstract of subjects. To study and do mathematics, you must remove your mind from the real world around you. In the process, you lose touch with reality. You don't see those stairs that you are approaching. You don't see the open file cabinet drawer. You don't see the students milling around after that exam with angry looks on their faces.

7. *But isn't mathematics good for your brain development?*

Is all exercise good for you? Is it good for your back to lift heavy boxes filled with safety goggles for hours at a time, day-in and day-out, for no apparent purpose? I think you know the answer is, 'no'.

Well, it's the same with brain exercise. You do difficult problems day-in and day-out, you could blow out your medulla oblongata, rip your brainstem, or split your hemispheres, permanently. Then where would you be?

And even if that didn't happen, you might overdevelop your brain, and it could end up looking like Arnold Schwarzennegger used to look, when he was dressed in a speedo and slathered in oil, glistening in the bright lights. Forgetting about the fact he married Maria Shriver and is now the governor of California, be honest. Is that how you want your brain to look?

So after doing your share of math, kick back at the end of the day. Forget about that lemma that's been driving you crazy. Go home, have a soda, and watch some reality TV shows. You'll be glad you did.

8. Why is safety the most important issue at NNWSU?

Each college and university strives to be the best it can be. Those of us at Northie have realized that we don't have a chance in hell of being the best in any academic discipline. So instead, we have decided to focus on safety. Our goal is nothing less than to be the safest educational institution in the country. Better than Harvard. Better than MIT. Better than Bluebonnet Hill Community College, that pretender to the safety crown right down the road.

Remember when you were a candidate for a faculty position in mathematics here? You probably thought you were being evaluated on the basis of your ability to teach and do research. Nothing could be further from the truth. In fact, you were being evaluated solely on the basis of your previous safety record and your future safety potential. During your job talk, we had a checklist. Shoes tied in a double knot? Zipper up? Pens carefully capped? You must have satisfied all the criteria on the checklist, as otherwise, you would not be reading this document. But don't think you can rest on your laurels. Tenure and promotion are also contingent on your attention to safety procedures.

Well, that concludes this initial discussion about safety in an arithmetic environment. We hope we haven't scared you with all of this talk of the dangers of mathematics. If you approach mathematics with an eye to safety, you may find it productive, and yes, perhaps even enjoyable.

We look forward to meeting you personally at our mandatory weekly math safety seminars, which begin soon. Look for our multi-colored notice coming in your mailbox shortly. But in the meantime, remember.

Safety: It's not just a word anymore.

This document brought to you compliments of the Northnorth-western State University Office of Office Safety (NNWSUOOS).

Trial and Error

Characters

Dr. Phipps

Prosecuting Attorney

Judge and narrator

Defense

Judge is at podium, chair in front of podium for Phipps. Defense attorney sitting at table.

Attorney: Please be seated, Mr. Phipps.

Phipps: Actually, it's Dr. Phipps.

Attorney: Really? Are you a medical doctor?

Phipps: No. But I have a Ph.D. That means I have a doctorate. So I should be addressed appropriately.

Attorney: And tell the court, Mr. Phipps, do you often insist on being called doctor?

Phipps: I prefer to be called that.

Attorney: Perhaps, because of some insecurity on your part? A need to assert your authority through a title?

Phipps: I want my students to know I am in control.

Attorney: And do you take some pleasure in that control, Mr. Phipps?

Defense: Objection, this is an irrelevant line of questioning.

Judge: Sustained.

Attorney: I retract the question. Now tell me, Mr. Phipps, were you the instructor for Math 105: Multivariable Calculus at Freedmont College this last fall?

Phipps: I was the professor for that course, yes.

Attorney: And was there a student named Jeffrey Foible in that class?

Phipps: Yes, there was.

Attorney: And do you see him here today in the courtroom?

Phipps: Yes, he is sitting over there next to his mother.

Attorney: And can you tell us how Jeffrey did in your class?

Phipps: He received a C+.

Attorney: Was he close to a B-?

Phipps: Yes. But he was clearly in the C+ range.

Attorney: I see. And how many students were in the course, Mr. Phipps?

Phipps: About 150.

Attorney: 150? With that many students, is it difficult to keep track of an individual student, and how they are doing in the course?

Phipps: I have teaching assistants.

Attorney: I see. And so they keep track of the individual students, relieving you of the necessity to do so?

Phipps: No, I pay attention, too. I review the grades on the homework and I do all the grading on the exams.

Attorney: Really? How much time does that take?

Phipps: On the two midterms, I spent about twelve hours grading each of them. Then, the final took longer. About twenty hours.

Attorney: Twenty hours? That's a tremendous amount of time to be sitting, staring at student work. It must be exhausting. Is it hard to keep up your concentration that long?

Phipps: I take breaks.

Attorney: You mean like getting a drink of juice, using the bathroom, maybe watching a little TV?

Phipps: Yes, that's right.

Attorney: And of course, you aren't going to complete twenty hours of grading in a day. I suppose it is stretched over a period of several days. How many days did it take you on the exam for this course?

Phipps: As I remember it, about three days.

Attorney: I see. That's quite a bit of time. So you might finish for one day, and then have a 12- or 15-hour break before resuming.

Phipps: Yes.

Attorney: Now, correct me if I'm wrong. After all, you're the math teacher. But 20 hours means 1200 minutes. Divide by 150 and that means an average of 8 minutes per exam.

Phipps: Yes, that's right.

Attorney: And how many pages were there on the final?

Phipps: Eight pages.

Attorney: So, a minute per page.

Phipps: Yes.

Attorney: And how many problems are on a page?

Phipps: About four, if each part of a multiple part question is counted separately.

Attorney: So 15 seconds a problem.

Phipps: About that, yes.

Attorney: And do you give partial credit?

Phipps: Oh, yes.

Attorney: Do you feel that in the 15 seconds you apportion to a given problem, you can fairly determine the appropriate amount of partial credit?

Phipps: Some problems take less than 15 seconds and some take more. When I need to think about how much to give, I take longer.

Attorney: Oh, and so some of the time when you are grading, you aren't thinking at all. Kind of on automatic pilot.

Phipps: There are some problems where there isn't much partial credit to give. Either they have the answer right or they do not.

Attorney: And do you consider yourself a consistent grader?

Phipps: I try.

Attorney: Do you know a Ms. Elaine Pleppmeyer?

Phipps: I believe she was a student in the course.

Attorney: Good for you, Mr. Phipps. It must not be easy getting to know all the students.

Phipps: I do my best.

Attorney: And can you tell me, is she seated in the courtroom right now?

Phipps: Well, um, I'm not sure.

Attorney: But I thought you knew her.

Phipps: Is that her over there, seated by Foible?

Attorney: No that is Jeffrey Foible's sister.

Phipps: How about the blonde woman by the door?

Attorney: No, that is not her.

Phipps: Then I am not sure.

Attorney: In fact, Mr. Phipps, Elaine Pleppmeyer is not here today. However I do have her final exam right here. Can you verify that this is her final exam from the course?

Phipps: Well, yes, it does appear to be her exam.

Attorney: I would like to enter this as Exhibit A. Can you tell the court, please Mr. Phipps, what grade appears at the top of the exam?

Phipps: It is a B-.

Attorney: And the numerical score?

Phipps: An 81.

Attorney: I see, and can you verify for the court that here I have a copy of Mr. Foible's final exam?

Phipps: Yes, that appears to be the exam.

Attorney: I would like to enter this as Exhibit B. Can you tell the court what grade and score is on this exam?

Phipps: It is a C+, with a score of 79.

Attorney: Interesting. Not so different, is it? Now tell me Mr. Phipps, and please feel free to consult your roll book, but other than this difference in their final exams, how close were the grades for these two students coming into the final?

Phipps: Well, Foible did slightly better on the homeworks, and Pleppmeyer did slightly better on the two midterms. They were both borderline between a B and a C.

Attorney: So you would characterize their performance up to the final as being essentially equivalent as far as their ultimate grade is concerned?

Phipps: Yes, that is true.

Attorney: Oh, dear, so it seems that this minor two-point difference between their scores on the final made the difference between Jeffrey Foible receiving a B and a C.

Phipps: Actually, a B- and a C+.

Attorney: Whatever. It is a big difference, Mr. Phipps. Perhaps the difference between getting into law school and not getting into law school?

Phipps: I don't know about that. I just give students the grades they deserve.

Attorney: Do you have any idea of the potential earning power that a lawyer has Mr. Phipps? Do you realize that this tiny two-point difference may have cost Mr. Foible five million dollars over his lifetime?

Phipps: That isn't my concern.

Attorney: Well, perhaps it should be, Mr. Phipps, because if you made a mistake in grading the exam, that could be a very costly mistake.

Phipps: What do you mean?

Attorney: Please open the exam to page 4. Let's take a look at Problem 11. Could you please read the problem to the court?

Phipps: It says, "Find the volume of the tetrahedron in the first octant of space bounded by the three coordinate planes and the plane $x + 2y + 3z = 6$."

Attorney: Thank you, Mr. Phipps. Perhaps you could explain the problem to us. After all, we are not all experts in calculus, like you are.

Phipps: Well, the three coordinate planes are the xy, the yz, and the xz plane, which are three orthogonal planes intersecting pairwise along the coordinate axes.

Attorney: I'm sorry. I must be slower than your students. Orthogonal? Intersecting pairwise?

Phipps: Umm. It's like the corner of a box. Three planes meeting perpendicularly. Then a fourth plane slices through and cuts off the corner of the box.

Attorney: Thank you. That makes a bit more sense. Now, you say the plane $x + 2y + 3z = 6$. So $x + 2y + 3z = 6$ is a plane.

Phipps: Yes, that is the equation of a plane.

Attorney: Oh, so it's not itself a plane. It is the equation of a plane. That seems like an important distinction.

Phipps: If you are going to be picky, then yes, it would be slightly more correct to say that $x + 2y + 3z = 6$ is the equation of a plane, rather than a plane itself.

Attorney: Well, perhaps when five million dollars is at stake, it would pay to be picky. Now, as I understand it, the tilted plane intersects the x, y, and z axes at 6, 3, and 2, respectively. Is that correct?

Phipps: Yes.

Attorney: Then the base is a right triangle with the two edges at the right angle of lengths 6 and 3. So it has area 9.

Phipps: That is correct.

Attorney: And the height of the tetrahedron is 2, so it appears you want the students to apply the famous formula for the volume of a tetrahedron, which is one third of the area of the base times the height. In this case, we obtain 6. Did I do that right?

Phipps: That is the correct answer, but no, I did not want them to use the formula for the volume of a tetrahedron. The whole point of the class is to learn calculus. They were supposed to create a double integral that gives the volume of the solid.

Attorney: You mean as in this solution given by Ms. Elaine Pleppmeyer, which we see on this overhead slide.

Phipps: Yes, that is what I intended. Only the upper limit of integration on that outer integral should be 6, not 3.

Attorney: I see, and that's why you took off two points out of the fifteen possible.

Phipps: Yes, that's right.

Attorney: Seems fair enough.

Phipps: It is a standard amount I took off for a mistake like that.

Attorney: Very good. Now, shall we look at Jeffrey Foible's solution? I have it on this next overhead slide. Well, look at that. He appears to have the correct solution 6. And he appears to have done it using the exact method I described. Can you tell us how many of the fifteen points you took off, and what it is you wrote on the exam?

Phipps: Umm, it looks like I took off 5 points. And I wrote in the margin, "Use calculus to solve these problems, not memorized formulas."

Attorney: So, correct me if I misunderstand. Ms. Pleppmeyer got the answer wrong, and you deducted two points, and Mr. Foible got the answer right, and you deducted five points.

Phipps: Well, yes. But he didn't use calculus.

Attorney: Oh, and can you point me to where on the exam it says that all problems must be solved using calculus?

Phipps: That was implied.

Attorney: Oh, I see. Implied?

Phipps: I did put on the front of the exam, "In all cases, grade is determined by the instructor."

Attorney: I see. And tell me, Mr. Phipps, if you wrote on the exam, "In all cases, grade to be determined by size of student's butt," would that then make it acceptable to determine the grade in that manner?"

Defense: Objection, your honor.

Judge: Sustained. The jury is instructed to ignore the word "butt". Strike it from the record.

Attorney: Let me rephrase the question. Are instructors not bound by some code of ethics? Should it not be the case that if a student gets the right answer, they should get the points they deserve?

Phipps: This was a calculus course. Students were supposed to learn calculus. We had done problems like that on the homework. They knew they were supposed to do the problem using calculus.

Attorney: And because Jeffrey Foible had this additional knowledge, because he had taken the time in his previous mathematical career to learn this formula, to remember this formula, you deducted five points?

Phipps: I don't believe he knew the formula.

Attorney: What do you mean?

Phipps: I think he copied it from Karen Lapala's paper.

Attorney: What makes you think that?

Phipps: Karen Lapala is an A student. She is the only other student in the entire class who used the formula to solve that problem. I think Foible didn't know how to do that problem, looked at her paper, and wrote down the answer. I think he cheated.

Attorney: Really? And do you know if Jeffrey Foible was sitting anywhere near Ms. Lapala during the exam?

Phipps: I can't be sure, but I have a vague recollection he was sitting near to her.

Attorney: Really? If you are right, you must have one of the most prodigious memories known to humankind. Let's see. With 150 people sitting in the auditorium, each person sitting next to say, two other people, how many pairs does that make? That's approximately 150 pairs that you would need to remember. You looked out at that mass of people and immediately memorized 150 pairs. Is that the case?

Phipps: No, I don't remember who everyone was sitting next to, but I think Foible was sitting next to Lapala.

Attorney: Forgive me if I seem skeptical that you could possibly remember that. But let me ask you this. Might your suspicion that Jeffrey Foible cheated off Ms. Lapala have influenced how many points you took off on his exam? Or perhaps, the better question is how many points did you take off on this problem on Ms. Lapala's exam?

Phipps: Um, I think I took off three.

Attorney: Three? But that isn't fair. After all, she and Mr. Foible had the same answer. Why should she lose only three points when he lost five? For all you know, she could have cheated off Mr. Foible.

Phipps: She had a picture of the tetrahedron.

Attorney: But nowhere in the problem did it say to draw the tetrahedron. Why are you giving points for it?

Phipps: It demonstrates that she understood what was going on. I gave partial credit for that.

Attorney: Come now, Mr. Phipps, do you really expect the jury to believe that by drawing random pictures on an exam, pictures that were not asked for, a student can receive points?

Phipps: Well, yes, because...

Attorney: If I draw a picture of a person for my Abnormal Psychology essay question on schizophrenia, should I get partial credit?

Phipps: Of course not, but...

Attorney: The truth, Mr. Phipps, is that you didn't take off more points for Mr. Foible because he failed to draw a tetrahedron. You took off the extra points because you had it in for him.

Phipps: Had it in for him? I barely knew him.

Attorney: My client recalls waking up one day in lecture, and you fixing him with a particularly malevolent stare. It was at this moment that he realized that you had it in for him.

Phipps: I didn't have it in for him. And even if I did, I couldn't have graded his exam more harshly. I grade blind.

Attorney: Do you mean to tell us that you grade your students' exams with your eyes closed?

Phipps: No, of course not. I mean that I flip over the cover sheet with the student's name on it before I ever start grading. Then when I grade a page, I have no idea which student is which. I cannot be influenced by my impressions of their abilities.

Attorney: Well, isn't that a clever idea. So you never know who it is that you are grading?

Phipps: That's right.

Attorney: But I suppose that once in a while, there is a student who has very distinctive handwriting, and sometimes, you are aware of who it is.

Phipps: Maybe once in a while.

Attorney: Perhaps, that was the case with Jeffrey Foible?

Phipps: I don't believe so.

Attorney: I would like everyone to direct their attention to the screen at right. On the overhead I have a sample of Jeffrey Foible's handwriting. Note how the c's have an unusually sharp curvature. And notice the angle between the two lines making up the x. That angle is 27.3245 degrees, approximately. However the national average is 29.2234. Am I right, Mr. Phipps that x's come up a lot on your exams?

Phipps: Yes, they do. But you can't believe that I would be able to recognize Foible's handwriting from these minor variations?

Attorney: Perhaps not consciously, Mr. Phipps, but the human mind is an incredibly intricate and subtle device. It is capable of much more than we give it credit for. Do you know that they say we use less than 10% of our possible brain capacity? What do you think the rest of our brain is doing?

Phipps: I have no idea.

Attorney: No, it does not appear that you do. Thank you, Mr. Phipps. You may step down. (*Phipps steps to the side. Attorney now speaks to the audience.*)

Members of the jury, this case now falls into your capable hands. And from my point of view, it is a relief to see it there. Because I believe you understand the critical importance of this trial.

Take a look at Jeffrey Foible, sitting there. Look at him. There sits a boy who was one of the best and the brightest, on the verge of manhood, ready to embark on his future. But what future is that? What future is left to him now?

Who was it that destroyed his confidence, who crushed his dreams, who thwarted him from following his rightful path? I think you know the answer to that. It was the defendant, Mr. Phipps.

Fifteen seconds! That's how long Mr. Phipps put into scoring each problem. Fifteen seconds. That's the amount of time he bequeathed, in his magnanimity, to determine the difference between the B grade that would get Jeffrey into law school and the C grade that shuts him out forever. Fifteen seconds. Does that sound fair to you? No, I'm betting it doesn't.

Now, of course, this case isn't just about compensating Jeffrey Foible for the suffering he has incurred. It is not about one student and the disastrous results of his professor's incompetence.

No, it is about how systematically, across this country, faculty destroy their student's hopes and dreams. It is about how the whim or mood of a professor can change the course of a student's life. How insults exchanged in a heated department meeting can generate emotions that alter the distribution of points on an exam. How a poorly digested bean burrito can cause a student to be barred from the career to which they have always aspired.

What happens when you put absolute power into the hands of a despot? When checks and balances don't exist? When one person has the unbridled authority to capriciously determine the fates of others?

I am not just asking you to chastise Mr. Phipps. I am asking you to send a message to all the teachers out there. To tell them that the age of tolerance for their misdeeds is over, once and for all.

Each and every one of you, members of the jury, knows what I am talking about. Because each and every one of you knows that when you were a student, you were unfairly graded. You did not receive the points you deserved, perhaps because your teacher had a head cold, or even worse, because your teacher didn't like the way you looked. Do the right thing. Do it for the millions of students who have gone before. Do it for the millions of students yet to come. And do it for Jeffrey Foible. Thank you for your attention.

Narrator/Judge: Doug Phipps jerked awake, his heart pounding. Throwing off the covers, he leaped out of bed and flicked on the desk lamp. He rifled through the pile of papers strewn about the desk until he found Foible's exam.

Flipping it open to the fourth page, he crossed out his written remarks and the circled −5, replacing them with a check mark. Then he flipped the exam closed, turned out the light, and settled back into bed. But sleep eluded him, and four hours later, as light began to stream through his windows, he looked forward to the day's grading with dread.

Hiring Season

Sept. 7: Everyone in the department seems to be getting along. People saying hello to one another at the faculty mailboxes. Past malice seems to have vanished, blown away by warm summer winds. Ganser and I are hopeful this year may be different.

Sept. 12: Classes underway. Ganser has finagled us both onto the hiring committee. Algebraists are upset that two topologists are members. Bullman and Klimkee are pushing for applied, Bullman because she is applied, and Klimkee because he is married to Bullman's sister.

Oct. 12: The hiring committee still can't come to agreement on whether to serve cookies or cheese and crackers at the meetings. Ganser just wants coffee. I prefer little frosted pink wafer cookies, but no one else concurs. Bullman and Klimkee are arguing for wine.

Oct. 23: The hiring committee chair and the recording secretary are no longer on speaking terms, meaning there are no minutes for the meetings. This allows committee members to say things they otherwise wouldn't dare.

Nov. 2: Ganser and I have enlisted the support of Costa, who, although not a topologist, has interests in Riemann surfaces. Perhaps we can broker a deal.

Nov. 12: Algebraists are no longer cooperating. Meetings are deteriorating. Bullman keeps kicking me under the table and then pretending it was accidental. It really hurts.

Nov. 14: Ganser says faculty in his neighboring offices are becoming rude. He is uncomfortable entering and leaving the building. I fear for the direction in which we are heading.

Nov. 18: Ganser and I threaten to look for jobs elsewhere. Klimkee offers to sign us up for the Math Employment Registry.

Dec. 1: Big blow. Costa went away for Thanksgiving and never came back. Rumor has it he's now an actuary.

Dec. 7: All-out war has commenced. Halls have become a wasteland, littered with crumpled letters of recommendation and strategically placed tacks. No hope of deciding this easily. Ganser and I have dug in for the long term. Ganser is determined, but I fear for his health. His hands have been shaking. He needs caffeine, and soon.

Dec. 10: Klimkee is divorcing Bullman's sister. Bullman and Klimkee now despise each other. Ganser and I take the opportunity to do a celebratory dance in the corridor. Quite a show, but no one's there to see it.

Dec. 15: The administration may have to step in. Work has come to a standstill. Even the students are afraid. Ganser and I are hunkered down in his office. Departmental communication reduced to email contact only, and most of it too coarse to repeat. Ganser continually paces, paces. This is almost as bad as last year.

Dec. 20: I tried to stop him, but Ganser was desperate. Risked all for java run. Grabbed a jar of instant out of the lounge. Brought back my mail, including the latest AMS *Notices*. Job listings are meager. Both despondent.

Dec. 22: Ceasefire has been declared. Nervously, Ganser and I attend the holiday party. Initially everyone is civil. Refreshments are a disappointment. No little frosted pink wafer cookies. Spirits low all around. We depart as yelling commences. Not much hope for the new year.

Jan. 2: Returnees look prepared for the long haul. Several carrying coffeepots. We are checking to see if the fire marshal may prevent it.

Jan 15: Ganser and I are holed up in my office. Ganser is screaming for coffee now. He's licked the instant jar clean. I'm feeding him chocolates and cola, but he's begging for Guatemalan Mocha Supreme.

Jan. 22: Algebraists have broken. Waving a white flag, they file out, headed for Starbucks most likely. Down to Applied versus Topology. Ganser drops in and out of lucidity.

Feb. 14: There is hope. Administration has promised funding for a fluid dynamics person, half in math, half in engineering, making topology the highest remaining priority. Ganser is elated. Chair calls to tell us the good news. Doesn't seem too angry we haven't met our classes in a month.

Feb. 29: On pins and needles. Department meeting slated for tomorrow. All will be in attendance. This could be it.

March. 11: It's official. Ganser and I have received permission to hire. We are jubilant.

March 29: Best candidates gone. We had three interview talks, and it's not clear any of them know the difference between a Möbius band and an annulus.

April 17: We have hired. Although he only speaks a Kurdish dialect, and he's actually in number theory, he does seem to be familiar with the torus, or so it appears from our communication via sign language.

May 13: Due to visa problems, our candidate cannot come after all. We will have to repeat the process next year. It is disappointing, but we consider it a learning process. Ganser has installed a cappucino machine in his office. All told, it could have been worse. One can only hope for the future.

Class Reunion

Well, if it isn't Cosine! I haven't seen you in 20 years. You look great. Still smooth as a baby's bottom. How do you do it?

Hey, I heard your wife left you. Sorry about that. So e^x is your ex. I hope you don't mind my saying, but she's an amazing function. I had a crush on her in high school. And I have to tell you, she hasn't aged a day. No one in her family has. I always had trouble differentiating between her and her mother.

I know you really loved her. Hey, you might want to take it easy on that punch. You know, there's rum in there.

Me? I'm not married. Never have been. Back in high school, with all the girlfriends I had, who would have guessed that Natural Log would still be single? But it's not like I'm incapable of a monogamous relationship. I am a one-to-one kind of guy. I just haven't met the right function. But I'm doing my best to meet as many as possible, if you know what I mean.

Hey, speaking of break-ups, did you hear about Step Function? Secant left him. Said she needed some continuity in her life. And get this. Now she's seeing Absolute Value. So the guy's continuous, but what about his derivative? Well, I guess it could be worse. At least he's Lipschitz.

Hey, look who's standing over there, talking to the Gauss map. It's Logistic Growth. Oh, is she hot. Did you hear? She's a model. Made it to the big time. Does all kinds of modeling. Drug dissipation, blood alcohol content, constrained population growth, disease spread. You name an important modeling assignment, she's there. Saw her on the cover of the *New England Journal of Medicine* last month.

And over there by the hors d'ouevres; it's Riemann Zeta. Remember, he was class president? You know, after high school he did the lawyer thing. But he got tired of it pretty quick. Found himself representing all kind of sleazy functions, some nowhere differentiable, some not even well defined. Decided he wanted to give something back to society. So he went into politics.

But you know, his first election was a tough one. He went up against the incumbent, some polynomial who was a functional illiterate as far as I could tell. There was all kind of mudslinging going on. Then the polynomial brings up the values issue. Challenges Riemann to divulge where his zeros occur. Makes a big deal out of it.

Personally, I didn't know what to think. How much privacy should a politician be allowed? Then Riemann gives this incredibly persuasive speech in which he posits that your zeros are your business, and it is the right of every function to decide whether or not to divulge where they occur. It was truly moving. So the electorate buys Riemann's hypothesis and he's elected. Now everybody wants to be like him; L-functions, Dedekind Zeta, you name it.

Hey, remember Arctan? I think she was in your homeroom. Did you hear she went to Wall Street? Works in derivatives. She's done extremely well for herself.

Uh-oh, speaking of Arctan, there's her old flame $1/(x^2+1)$. Look the other way. Poor guy. Had some substance-abuse issues. He was completely dysfunctional. Now he's trying to integrate himself back into society, but you can guess the chances of that. He's no Arctan.

And of course there was also his brother, $x^2 + 1$. Did you hear about him? So naïve. One night, he fell in with some polynomials defined over $Q[i]$. They got him toasted, lead him down a dark alley and in the morning, all the police found were his factors.

Hey, maybe you should switch to soda water. You are starting to list. You know, life is full of ups and downs. You'll find someone else. Sheesh, listen to me, telling you about ups and downs. Like you have never had time as the variable on your horizontal axis.

Look, over by the registration table. There's Gamma. What an athlete he was, huh? Captain of the football *and* the wrestling teams. You know he went to college. Got a full scholarship to Western Harmonic. Everyone assumed he would pledge Gamma Gamma Gamma, but instead he went Tri Delta with his buddies Dirac and the Laplacian. Now that Laplacian, he was an operator.

Hey, how do you like the band? I booked them. They're called Dr. Dedekind and the Minor Functionaries. I always liked func.

Now look who's stuffing himself with pigs in a blanket. None other than Phi, or as he insists, Euler's Totient Function. Talk about pretentious. Totient's not even a word. What an asymptote. I heard he was dating your ex, but I find it hard to believe. She's way too classy for him.

Whoops. Dropped your glass. Not that anybody cares. What's a broken glass here or there?

So you keeping busy? I'm still getting lots of work. Some physics, some engineering, a little pure math. I don't know if you saw it, but I even had a cameo appearance in "A Beautiful Mind".

Hey, if you get a chance, you should go next door. The Series are having their reunion. Talk about wild. Taylor Series was doing his imitation of Maclaurin. "Look at me. $a = 0$. dumdedumdedum." I laughed so hard I squirted Sprite out my nose. Those guys know how to party. It would do you good. Put a smile on your face.

Hey, there's Cube Root. I sat behind her in algebra. Always had a thing for her. I think I'll go say hello, see what she's up to now. With any luck, she's available. Anyway, it's been great talking with you. Good luck with the alcohol thing. Catch you at the next one.

Worst-Case-Scenario Survival Handbook: Mathematics

Introduction

By its very nature, mathematics is a risky endeavor. You may have already experienced injury—physical or psychological—from attempts to learn mathematics, or perhaps just from living a mathematical lifestyle. To help ward off further peril, we have compiled the following scenarios with the help of our experts. But keep in mind that the safest course is always to consult a Ph.D. mathematician. UNDERTAKE THE ACTIVITIES IN THIS ARTICLE ON YOUR OWN ONLY WHEN NO PH.D. IS AVAILABLE. The publisher, author, and experts disclaim liability from harm caused by the use of the information contained in this article. Good luck!

How to Give a Job Talk

Unless you are Gauss, at some point you will have to give a job talk. This is perhaps the most important talk you will ever give, so unless you want to teach Remedial Fractions for the rest of your life, consider following these instructions for the various sections of your talk.

First quarter: Start off simply, defining your terms carefully and drawing lots of pictures, lulling the audience into the impression they might understand the talk. Then continue to build one definition on top of another, each dependent on the previous one. Lots of Greek letters, arrows, and supersubsuperscripts give an impression of intellectual depth.

Second quarter: Include numerous theorems, corollaries, and lemmas. Number them, making it easier for the audience to keep track of the running total. In passing, mention the names of as many members of the department as possible. If someone's work is related only because the two areas start with the same letter, that's good enough reason to include them.

Third quarter: This is where you make the talk incomprehensible to everyone, including yourself. If you can understand it, someone else might, in which case it cannot be serious work. Of course, making the talk sufficiently incomprehensible is not difficult. A selection of paragraphs from three or four randomly chosen papers out of an old issue of *Matematicheskie Issledovaniya* of the Akademiya Nauk Republiki Moldova usually does the trick.

Last quarter: Here is where you make it sound like you are on the verge of solving the greatest two or three problems in mathematics. Just a year or two more, and whatever institution has had the foresight to hire you will be basking in your reflected glory.

And then, after making this point, whatever you do, end on time. This is the most sacred of all rules. Ending on time is the human equivalent of rolling over on your back and exposing your neck. If you do not end on time, you are implying that you believe you are more important than they are. And your chances of being hired then drop to epsilon, which in this case is an exceedingly small number.

How to Escape from a Sinking Department

Your department is floundering. It has lost its VIGRE grant. The state legislature has cut the budgets. Salaries have been frozen, and the university is shrinking the size of the department while the enrollments remain high. You need to make the leap to a different school. Here are the simple steps to follow:

1. Choose the school to which you wish to jump. Spend a sabbatical there, so they have a chance to get to know you, unless that would be to your disadvantage.

2. Prepare your curriculum vita beforehand. Bulk it up with papers, notes, and technical reports. Often a single paper can make more than one appearance in a variety of guises. Even an erratum to a paper can add to the length of the vita if carefully titled (e.g., *Notes on the Work of* ...).

3. Wait until both departments are almost at the same level. Do not WAIT to jump until your department is already in the dumpster. Then it is too late. As your department deteriorates, and the department to which you wish to jump improves, there will be a moment when the two are comparable. It is the instant before then that you must jump.

4. Typically, the landing may be bumpy. Expect resentment on the part of members of your new department who do not appreciate the addition of a senior member in an area unrelated to their own interests. A disgruntled chair may give you unpleasant teaching assignments for the first few years. But very quickly, you will be absorbed into the fabric of the department.

5. If you are the cause of departmental decline, then keep in mind that you will have to jump again very soon.

How To Survive a Counterexample from the Audience

You are delivering a keynote address at the National Mathematics Meetings when an audience member interrupts to point out an obvious counterexample to your main theorem.

1. Remain calm. Do not break down in tears or run from the room.

2. Make it clear that you understand this material to a depth this interloper could never hope to achieve. For instance, say, "Of course your example does not apply. Your space is not Hasselhof."

If the audience member asks the definition of Hasselhof, act incredulous. Do not admit that it is meaningless beyond being the name of the actor David Hasselhof of "Baywatch" fame. Simply say, "How can I be expected to have a fruitful conversation with someone who is not familiar with Hasselhoficity." Then storm out of the room.

Analysis: What matters is not the correctness or incorrectness of your theorem. What matters is the permanent impression formed in the minds of the audience. Better to shoulder through, and present the appearance of being fully in control of the situation. Later, appropriate "additional hypotheses" can be added to make the theorem true, vacuously if necessary.

How to Survive a Lecture to your Daughter's Second Grade Class

There are several simple rules for speaking on mathematics to an unusually young audience.

Rule 1: Bring candy. Offer to hand it out only when they are quiet.

Rule 2: Wear colorful clothing. Consider a red rubber ball on the end of your nose.

Rule 3: Talk down to their level. Know your audience. If you wish to speak about Haar Measure, speak about Lebesgue measure instead. If you want to explain exotic n-spheres, stick to dimension 7.

Rule 4: Know when to stop. Never run over into recess, or you might have a riot on your hands.

How to Survive Running Over a College Administrator

1. Do not panic. You have tenure.

2. Stop the car, get out, and call frantically for help. Act very concerned.

3. Ride with the administrator in the ambulance. Take this opportunity to explain to him or her the transforming effect you have had on the field of subliminal jet bundles.

4. Once at the hospital, offer to donate a kidney. It is unlikely a kidney will be necessary but the gesture will make you look good. If the offer is accepted, excuse yourself to use the bathroom, sneak out the window, and change professions. It's not worth a kidney.

Into Thin Air

I was up above the Lickorish Ridge, having traversed the difficult Casson-Gordon Step, and was resting on a small lemma on the North Face of the Poincaré Conjecture. As far as I knew, no one had been up this high before, and I felt like I had a good chance of finding a route all the way to the top. I was still breathing hard and the adrenaline was pumping through me. Those last fifty feet had been treacherous. A few times, my logic had slipped, and I had barely managed to grab a handhold and then scrabble onto solid footing. But now that I was up here, the view was incredible. The sky was an unnatural blue.

As I sucked air, I looked out into the distance. The Mathematical Range stretched beneath me. There were some of the peaks poking through the clouds upon which I first tested my mettle. Point Set Topology looked so tiny in comparison to where I sat now, but at the time, it had been a struggle. And there was Teichmüller Theory. I would have never made it up that slag heap if it weren't for McLuten. I was so naive then. So many mistakes. McLuten must have saved my rear a dozen times. If it weren't for him, I would be lying at the bottom of some crevasse, crumpled up on some counterexample to a laughable conjecture.

McLuten had seemed invincible then. He'd climbed all kinds, the big ugly granite slabs that rose up out of the undulating planes of geometry, the treacherous ice-covered theorems that kept us all in awe of algebra, and the crumbly rocks of the Analysis Range, where one false step could bring a mountain of epsilons and deltas down upon you. And McLuten had the look, too; the grizzled visage that resembled the crags and rocks he confronted daily, his eyes always focused on the next challenge.

I missed him. But he wasn't the kind that could ever be satisfied with all that he had accomplished. Had to go after the big one, the one they call Fermat.

They found him at the bottom of the Euler Face. Everyone had said that there was no way up Euler, but McLuten couldn't be dissuaded. He left three ABD's behind, with no means of support.

It wasn't but ten years later that Wiles made the summit. But Wiles had prepared. For seven years, he prepared. He knew the Euler Face was insanity. He came up Taniyama-Shimura, a route that had been championed by Ribet. And he did it alone.

It made Wiles an instant celebrity. He had tackled the big one. He had proved that no mountain was invincible. But that wasn't why he had done it. No, that's not why any of us did it.

And here I was, three quarters of the way up Poincaré. One of the largest unconquered peaks in the world. One of the few remaining giants of mathematics. Who would have thought that I would have a shot?

The wind was picking up a bit and wispy clouds scudded by. Suddenly a head bobbed up at the edge of the lemma. I jumped back. It was Politnikova. She pulled herself up over the edge, and lay there, trying to catch her breath.

"What the hell are you doing here?" I exclaimed. Politnikova waved me off as she gasped for breath. Not a lot of oxygen up here.

"Did you follow me up Geometrization Conjecture Ridge? Nobody knew I was even considering it."

Politnikova pulled off her goggles and sat up, still gasping, waving for me to wait.

"Relax, relax," she said in her thick Russian accent. "I did not come up the Geometrization Conjecture Ridge. I followed Poenaru's Route up the Clasp Trail and then over the Haken Ice Field."

"But everyone's tried that route. That's where Fourke disappeared."

"Yes, but Fourke was using out-of-date equipment, technology from the 50's. I am using the latest technology. Makes a difference."

"I can't believe this. I get up this high on Poincaré only to find you."

"And what is so wrong with me, huh?"

"You know perfectly well what I mean. I was going to do it on my own."

"Oh, yes, sure," said Politnikova smiling. "You would have no trouble single-handedly climbing those logical outcroppings up there." She pointed almost straight up.

"Well, I hadn't figured it all out yet."

"Yes, but two could work together to get around those problems. A little combinatorics, I'm good at combinatorics. A little geometry. You are good at geometry. And bingo, we are there."

"Well, I suppose you have a point," I said reluctantly. "Maybe we could work together."

Politnikova began to smile, but the smile froze as she jerked her head up. "Do you hear that?" she said, terror in her face. I pulled my hood away from my ear, and cocked my head to the side. In the distance, I could hear it, a slight rumble, but it was growing fast. "Oh, no," I said. "Avalanche!"

When I had been down at base camp, I had seen how precariously balanced the various arguments were that made up this face of the Poincaré Conjecture. A little bit of a shift here or there, and the whole mountainside could come down in your face. And that was the reality we were confronting. In that split second, we both knew that our dream of conquering Poincaré that day was over. But all that was suddenly irrelevant. Now it was a question of survival.

"We don't have a chance in hell if we stay here on this lemma. There isn't going to be a lemma in another two minutes," I screamed. "Throw your rope over the side, and if we can make it down to Bing's Theorem, we can hide behind that." I flipped Politnikova's rope onto

a piton I had already hammered into the rocks, clipped her on the
line and shoved her over the edge, before she could stop me. Then
I clipped on and jumped out into space. We zinged down the rope,
burning glove leather, until we hit the end of the rope. Up above,
the roar was deafening. When we hit the bottom of the rope, we just
unclipped and started rolling down the slope. All those hard-earned
steps, for naught, I thought as I careened downward. I rolled to a
halt twenty feet from Bing's Theorem, battered but in one piece. I
glanced up at where the lemma had been, only to see it disappear
entirely in the torrent of arguments that were cascading down upon
us. Politnikova grabbed my hood and pulled me toward Bing's Theorem. We managed to duck behind it just as the avalanche reached
us. Huddled there, we saw several years' worth of mathematics slam
past. It only lasted another minute, and then it was all gone. We
both sat in stunned silence and then Politnikova turned to me.

"We are lucky to be alive. Thank God for Bing's Theorem."

"Yup," I said. I knew Bing's Theorem would hold, if anything
would.

I looked up to where we had been perched moments before, and
the face was smooth as ice. No lemma, no corollary, not a handhold
to be had.

"We will not be getting up there that way," said Politnikova.

"Nope," I agreed. "This face is officially a dead end, starting
today."

I stood wearily, feeling the bruises and scrapes. "We should head
down," I said, "before any other arguments collapse."

Politnikova stood slowly. "Don't look so sad. We were higher up
there than anyone else has ever been."

"Yeah?" I said. "No one will believe it anyway. There isn't a
trace of where we were."

"Yes, but what matters is what we know, not what others think.
Hey, you come down to my tent, and I give you some very good
vodka."

I laughed. In a place where every ounce counts for survival, only
Politnikova would bring vodka.

"Sure," I said. I took one last look toward the peak, enshrouded in clouds now, not even visible anymore.

"We have vodka, and we talk," she said, "and maybe we figure out some other route to the top. Maybe we use Ricci flow. Hamilton knows what he is doing. We do that, too."

"Sure," I shrugged. "Why not?" We started down the mountain.

Math Talk

by Colin Adams and Lew Ludwig

Plug: Hello and welcome to *Math Talk*, with Plug and Chug, the Handwaving Brothers. We're coming to you this week from the Bruhat-Tits Building in our fair city. If you have a question about math, proof repairs, or anything remotely numerical, call us at 888-271-1729.

Chug: What a boring number! It doesn't even spell anything. We need a new number!

Plug: Yeah, go talk to Ramanujan! Hello and welcome to *Math Talk*.

Lenny: Yeah, this is Lenny from Konigsberg.

Chug: Now there's a great town! Len what's up?

Lenny: I have this 1982 theorem I picked up as a post doc at the Mittag-Leffler Institute and she's been a real work horse for years.

Chug: Yeah, those Swedes know how to build 'em.

Plug: Good safety record too.

Lenny: That's for sure. We've seen a lot of corollaries and conjectures together. Anyway, the other day I thought I'd take her for a spin down to the local seminar—it was around dusk.

Plug: Let me guess—a counterexample?

Lenny: How did you know?

Chug: They're really bad this time of year—especially around dawn and dusk—it's their mating season.

Plug: You ever seen two counterexamples mate? It's not pretty.

Chug: I don't even want to think about it. Go on...

Lenny: Well, I was coming around this curve and BOOM, there it was. We took it right in the front end. There were symbols strewn all over the pavement. I pulled to the side of the road and the theorem just collapsed. It looked liked some of the lemmas took it pretty hard.

Plug: How's the rear end?

Lenny: The corollaries seem OK, but what good are they without the lemmas?

Chug: So then what?

Lenny: Well, I called a friend and he came and got us to the seminar. The chalk monkeys looked it over and said the front end could be repaired, but it was going to take a lot of work. Three of the five lemmas are shot and the other two are leaking ordinals.

Plug: (Whistles) Sounds steep.

Lenny: Yeah, they're thinking at least a semester of seminars, lots of coffee, and release time just for starters. They're talking big bucks, NSF-sized bucks...

Plug: So I bet you want some advice on that classic question—Do I fix up my old faithful friend...

Chug: ...or go looking for something new and more dependable? As the former owner of a 1965 classic, The Blackboard Beauty as I called her, I'd fix this baby up.

Plug: That old pile of calcium carbonate? Give me a break. Listen, Lenny, the technology has improved so much since this thing came out, not to mention the efficiency of the new models. I'd go shopping... maybe something Japanese...a little topology number.

Lenny: Thanks—I'll give it a shot.

Plug: Good luck.

Chug: You'll need it!

Plug: And even though the 17-gon on Carl Friedrich Gauss's tombstone rolls over when we say it, this is MPR—Mathematical Public Radio. Let's go to our next caller. Hello, you're on *Math Talk*.

Penny: Hi, this is Penny from Cambridge.

Plug: Hi, Penny, what's shakin'?

Penny: Well, I'm trying to finish my dissertation, but I recently ran into a gap in one of the major results.

Chug: Uh oh, that's not good.

Penny: Tell me about it. I've taken it to every seminar in town with no luck. I got a few suggestions, but they were all dead ends. So, the other night I was working on it at the blackboard in my office, when I sensed someone looking over my shoulder. It was Will, our janitor. Out of the blue, he pointed at my induction step and said to replace every k with a $k + 1$. Then he disappeared down the hall. Said he had to hunt down the mop.

Chug: Did you give it a shot?

Penny: I thought, "What the heck, nothing else is working!" So I tried it and it worked! But I have no idea why. Is this just a fluke or what?

Plug: You know, I've seen cases like this in the past. I'm not sure why, and I wouldn't do it myself, but it does seem to work sometimes.

Chug: Ahhh! The quasi-mathematical, folkloric solution... I like it! Who knows why it works?

Penny: So what should I do?

Chug: LaTeX that sucker up and submit it before anyone notices! And if anyone does, you didn't talk to us!

Plug: As much as it hurts me too say so, I'd have to agree with my brother on that one. Send us a picture of your hooding ceremony!

Good luck, Penny—thanks for your call. We have time for one more call. Hello and welcome to *Math Talk*.

Karen: Hello, this is Karen from Tuscon. I'm sending my son off to college in the fall.

Chug: And a lot of money, I'll bet!

Karen: That's for sure! I'm calling to see if you can recommend a good calc book for him, because I know he'll need one.

Plug: Karen, tell us a little about your son. Does he like to discover things on his own, using computers, and write complete sentences about his results? Has he ever been to reform school?

Chug: Or is he a no-nonsense kind of guy who just loves working through a ton of problems that have tidy answers? Does he like tradition?

Karen: Hmmm... I know he really likes computers and his writing is so-so... but he also likes things very predictable.

Plug: Well, there are some middle-of-the-road models that come with CDs, which will appeal to his fondness of computers, but most of the problems are fairly straightforward with tons of examples.

Chug: Yeah—no longwinded, "open-ended" problems, as they call them.

Karen: Goodness, my son is definitely not "open ended!"

Plug: Sounds like the middle-of-the-road model is for him. Just go to our Shameless Commerce Division, click on the PPIS (Publishers Playing It Safe) icon and pick the one with the snazziest cover!

Chug: And don't forget to buy the student solution manual, companion website access card, and combination MP3, CD, DVD, Tetris player.

Plug: He means get him a decent calculator. He'll need something to amuse himself during the lectures!

Chug: See ya, Karen!

Plug: Well, you've done it again! You've just squandered another perfectly good hour listening to *Math Talk*.

Chug: Our producer, who points out regularly that we don't know what we are talking about, is Vic Torfield. Our Commuter Car Pool Coordinator is Abe Elian. Our Financial Growth Analyst is Nat U. Rullog. Our Orientation Coordination Team consists of Moe B. Uzband and Ann Ewlus. Our Russian Equality Control Supervisor is F.N. Knownlieff. His legal consultants are Nessen, Sairy, and Safishin, known to the denizens of Harvard Square as Nessy, Hairy, and Scary.

Plug: Thanks for listening and remember, don't derive like my brother!

Chug: Don't derive like my brother!

Plug: See ya' next week. Bye!

A Deprogrammer's Tale

They hooked him in calculus class. Started slow. Didn't want to be too obvious. Gave him a little trig review, some functional notation, and then introduced limits. Gave him lots of problems to work on. Kept him busy to get his guard down. Then pow, they hit him with the concept of the derivative. The raw power and simplicity of the idea. It was overwhelming. How could he resist? Who can? I know. I've been through it myself. Yes, that's right. I was one of them once. I was a slave to mathematics.

But unlike most, I escaped. And now my life is dedicated to helping others who were not as fortunate as I.

In this particular case, I was hired by the parents of one Lawrence Desenex. One minute, Larry was pre-med, heading for a lucrative plastic surgery practice in Cherry Hill, and the next minute he was talking about earning a Ph.D. in mathematics. All thought of financial gain went out the window. His parents were horrified. Dreams of "my son, the doctor" turned into nightmares of "my son, the itinerant mathematician". But me, I wasn't surprised when I heard the tale. I'd heard it a hundred times before. Believe it or not, 1200 people a year get Ph.D.'s in math in the United States alone. That sounds incredible, but I understand why. I know the seductive power of a beautiful proof, the appeal of a well-turned lemma.

Larry had fallen prey in the usual manner. After hearing the derivative explained in a lecture hall with 300 other students, he went to see the professor during office hours. That's when they know they have you. You're one of the susceptible ones, looking for some meaning beyond the plug-and-chug problems.

A little chit chat, maybe notational, a bit of history, Newton versus Liebniz, that sort of thing, all seemingly innocuous. And then, when he least expected it, the epsilon delta definition of a continuous function. Poor guy was putty in the professor's hands. Before he could get his head back on straight, the professor invited him to a departmental colloquium, followed by tea. Larry dutifully went, and although he was blown out of the water by the material, he saw the others there, in rapt attention, lapping up the mathematical morsels.

At tea, the department members ignored Larry, feigning indifference to the freshman who was interested in math, pretending they were too wrapped up in their own research to care. But, oh, if only he knew they were watching his every move, as they scribbled on the blackboard and talked about this theorem or that with their colleagues. He was a marked man and Larry didn't even know it.

In cases like these, there is a small window of opportunity, a short period when a student can still be saved. But you must act fast. Once the student takes Real Analysis and Abstract Algebra, their fate is sealed. The window has been slammed shut and shuttered.

But his parents had called me in time. Larry was taking Linear Algebra, the applied version. There was hope yet.

I found him in the cafeteria with an untouched plate of tuna casserole and a copy of "The Man Who Loved Only Numbers" open in front of him. I gave him my winningest smile.

"Erdős, huh? Mind if I join you?"

He was clearly impressed, and motioned to the seat across the table.

"Like math, do you?" I asked.

"Oh, yes," he said enthusiastically. "It's so beautiful."

"Yes, it does have an appeal."

"Have you ever seen the argument for the uncountability of the reals?" he asked. "That's really cool." The bubbly excitement, the glassy bright eyes. Oh, he was in deep. We talked math for a while. I played along. Euclid this, Euler that. Then I laid the trap.

"Hey, my roommate and I are having a birthday celebration for Karl Friedrich Gauss on Wednesday at my apartment. You're invited."

Of course, he was thrilled. Susceptible and trusting are two descriptions of the same attribute.

He showed up right on time. It hadn't taken him long to pick up that characteristic of mathematicians. I let him in and locked the door behind him. Then everyone popped out, his parents, his grandparents, a cousin, an aunt, his best friend from high school.

"What's going on here?" he said, clearly at a loss. "This isn't a birthday party for Gauss."

"No, it's not," I said. "Gauss was born in April. This is an intervention, Larry. These are the people who love you and they're here to help." He backed away.

"Open the door. Let me go," he cried desperately. I blocked him.

"Not until you hear what we have to say."

He looked like Galois after the duel. The blood drained from his face. Must have been wondering where his muse was now.

His mother spoke first. "Bunchkins, bunchkins, have you thought about us? We love you, Pinchy, but good gracious, what would the neighbors say? Mrs. Krawlick would revel in the news. Our son, a mathema, a mathema.... I can't say the word."

She began to bawl uncontrollably. Larry's father held her. "Look at your mother. Look at what you are doing to her. She can't even say the word."

"Poor, poor, Erma," said his aunt, patting his mother on the sleeve.

"Larry, I can't believe you would do this. You seemed like you were a good kid. You used to watch television. You had a lemonade stand. What happened to you? My kids would never do this. Evan here, now he is a dentist, aren't you Evan?"

The cousin nodded yes.

"And Cybil works in marketing for an ad agency. And I am proud of them both."

"What about Karen?" asked Larry.

The aunt turned bright red. "How dare you mention her name in my presence."

Evan laughed. "Karen has a masters degree in accounting." Not my area, but I sympathized.

Larry's best friend spoke up. "Listen Larry. The problem is, it's not cool to do math. Business degrees, they're cool. You know, internet start-ups and all. Theater degrees, that's cool. You wear black clothes and talk about Pinter. But math? It's not cool. Nothing is cool until everyone is doing it."

Larry wrung his hands.

"You don't understand. I don't have a choice. I am not choosing to do mathematics. Math has chosen me. When I saw that epsilon delta definition of continuity, it was like I had known it all my life. Here is what the professor was really talking about when he drew all those pictures. This is a rigorous definition. It felt so good. It's not up to me anymore."

"Look, Larry," I said. "Do you want this to be you?" I showed him the pictures of mathematicians, the addicts with their white pallor from sitting under fluorescent lights for years at a time. Some were barely able to lift their eyes from the books in front of them as the camera clicked away. Their clothes, stained with coffee, made it clear they were unaware that fashion was an evolving concept.

But he was unmoved. "That's exactly what I want to be," he said.

I sighed. "Okay, Larry, I have no choice anymore." I strapped him into the barcalounger and turned on the TV. I kept him there for two weeks. Mostly reruns of the *Brady Bunch* and *Welcome Back*

Kotter. By the time we were done, spittle dripped from the side of his mouth. His brain had been washed clean.

Unfortunately, it had been washed so clean that medical school was no longer an option. Larry did go on to a successful career with Seven Eleven, primarily mopping up the slushy spills at the Cherry Hill store. And I know that he's happier for it.

But Larry's story is just one story among many. These dangers are real. Do you know where your children are? Are you sure they are watching TV, and not sitting in on a seminar, or leafing through a math text?

If we are vigilant, we can prevent mathematics from spreading any further. But we will need to fight the minions of mathematics at every turn. We will need the entertainment industry to hype style over intellectual curiosity. We will need to inundate children with the belief that being good at math is something to be ashamed of. We will need to convince everyone that there is nothing wrong with mathematical illiteracy. So far, so good.

Research Announcement

BiPhdMA seeks same for long weekends of commutative algebra, including walks in the woods discussing math, candlelit dinners over some excellent local rings, and tranquil evenings spent staring into the fire as we contemplate ideals. Tired of the conference scene? Sincere mathematicians only need respond. Let's trade papers and see where it goes from there.

Code:

Bi: Gender irrelevant

Phd: Ph.D.

M: Mathematician

A: Algebraist

Dear BiPhdMA,

I'm not the kind of mathematician who answers personal ads, but I found yours intriguing. I have included a reprint of an article I wrote on birational extensions as well as some jottings on maximal ideals of formal fiber rings. What do you say we get together over a few lemmas and see where it goes from there?

Ahmad

Dear Ahmad,

I can't tell you how much I enjoyed our time together. Your lemmas have a certain swagger, pushing the mathematical envelope as they do. And when you finally stated your proposition, I thought I would swoon. Who would have thought that Noetherian rings could behave so badly? Thank you for making me look forward to each new day, and the mathematics that it will contain.

Yours,

Craig

Dear Craig,

I too had a wonderful time. I find myself thinking about how you showed that the associated prime ideal in that localization of a polynomial ring needn't be embedded. I cannot get it out of my head. I am impatiently waiting for the next time we can meet.

With greatest affection for your mathematics,

Ahmad

Craig Dearborn and Ahmad Ashanti announce the initiation of a collaboration on research on the Formal Fibers of Excellent Rings. The union will be celebrated with a tag-team talk at 4:00 on Saturday, June 11, to be followed by tea and cookies.

Craig Dearborn and Ahmad Ashanti announce the birth of their newest result,

Theorem 1.7, born at 11:42 A.M., Monday, December 11, 1999, weighing in at 7 ounces. It has been named the Dearborn Ashanti Rigidity Theorem.

Well, we never thought we would be writing one of these letters, but so much has happened this year, and we finally had to face up to the fact we wouldn't be able to personally contact all of you whom we hold dear.

It has been quite a year for us. January started things off with a bang, when it was announced that Theorem 1.7 [The Rigidity Theorem] would be appearing in the *Annals of Mathematics*. You can imagine the thrill. Craig's theorem from a previous collaboration, Theorem 2.2.1 [Dearborn-Kawauchi 3] has had a great year as well, having been cited in no fewer than three papers. And the big news is that we will be expecting a new arrival in August, although a few details still have to be worked through.

Craig has been elected to the editorship of the *Rhode Island Journal of Mathematics* (RIJM), a dream of his for many years. And Ahmad has been no slouch either, having refereed no fewer than fifteen papers this year, three for journals other than the RIJM. Quite the popular referee. Here's hoping your year has been as fruitful as ours.

With Best Holiday wishes,

Craig and Ahmad

Hope this holiday letter finds you in better spirits than we are experiencing around here this year. A small logical inconsistency was discovered in Theorem 1.7 [The Rigidity Theorem], and it has not been doing well ever since. It appears the inconsistency is spreading and all attempts at treatment have failed. But we are ever hopeful.

Craig has resigned the editorship of the *Rhode Island Journal of Mathematics* in order to spend more time with the Rigidity Theorem. Ahmad has been helping out when he can, but the complete homomorphic images property, and its implications for excellent rings, is taking up a lot of time.

Season's Best,

Craig and Ahmad

Retraction: Craig Dearborn and Ahmad Ashanti are saddened to report that Theorem 1.7 has been retracted, an announcement of which will appear in the *Annals of Mathematics*. In lieu of flowers, donations should be sent to the Centennial Fellowships of the American Mathematical Society.

This year, our research program seems to have stalled. We have consulted with various experts. They agree that this area is still fertile ground, and have no explanation for why we are not producing. Most likely, we just need to get back into the rhythm.

Unfortunately, that will be difficult, as Ahmad will be spending the spring semester in Australia where he will be working with the excellent ring theorists at Melbourne University. Then he will be in Berkeley for the summer. Craig is obligated to stay home and finish up several joint preprints, but his heart will be in Melbourne.

Our Best to You,

Craig and Ahmad

Surveillance Report:

Aug. 12, 11:32: Subject Ahmad Ashanti was seen entering the Mathematical Sciences Research Institute with Australian mathematician Hugh Rubenstein. Discussion appeared animated. Telephoto lens caught subject and Rubenstein taking turns writing equations vigorously on the blackboard. It appears that an exchange of preprints did occur.

These papers, filed with the American Mathematical Society, officially announce the cessation of collaboration between Craig Dearborn and Ahmad Ashanti. The reprints of their joint papers will be divided as follows: 40% for Dearborn, 40% for Ahmadi, and 20% for the lawyers. All future correspondence on the joint work should be directed to the law firm of Rudin & Rudin.

BiPhdMA seeks same for long-term research relationship. Seeking a book-level commitment here. Researchers trolling for a fast paper or two need not apply.

A Killer Theorem

The name's Mangum. Mangum, P.I. That's right. I'm a principal investigator on a National Science Foundation grant, of the mathematical variety. You need a PI, you call me. I'm in the book.

That's how this particular case came my way. It was a late spring afternoon, and the constant California sun was trying to weasel its way through the cracks in the mini-blinds hanging in my office windows at UCLA. I was busy filling my briefcase with a stack of papers that I wouldn't read that night when the phone rang. Only this particular call was not of the usual variety. Most often, it's a co-author suspecting his partner of co-authoring around. Wanting me to get proof. Or a chair who believes her department members are using office phones for personal business and wants the evidence so she can hang 'em out to dry. But this was different. It was Solomon Schmishmitt, a captain in the LAPD. The letters LAPD stand for the Los Angeles Police Department rather than some clever acronym for an outlandish mathematical organization. I know you were expecting otherwise, but in this business you have to learn to expect the expected, even when you expect it the least.

I knew Sol from the old days. We had been grad students together at Chicago. I majored in math. He majored in scotch. The last time I saw him, he was lying in the gutter outside the math building, in the pouring rain, too drunk to come inside and take his oral exams. Now that's drunk.

When I went on to a post doc at UCLA, I heard he finally dried out. Gave up the drinking, too. He realized that math wasn't his cup of tea, so he got a degree in law enforcement from an on-line police academy. Printed his diploma on a color printer, and got a job in LA. Since then, he had stayed on the straight and narrow and built up a reputation as a good cop. Because of his grad school days, they gave him the math beat.

After reminiscing about the various gutters he had spent time in, he got down to business.

"Listen, Dirk, I need your help. We have three dead algebraists."

"I know some departments that would be thrilled with that news," I replied.

"Most departments wouldn't want to lose one of these. Maclaunders, Honeykey, and Nakanimji."

The Holy Trinity. If algebraists marked fire hydrants like dogs, those three could soak down the Eiffel Tower, the Taj Mahal, and the Kremlin and still have plenty left over for actual fire hydrants.

"That's quite a group of algebraists," I said, "no pun intended."

"None taken."

"So let's hear the story. Were they at a conference?"

"That's just it. They weren't together at the time. They were each at their home institutions when they died. About as far apart as you could pick three points on the face of the earth."

Although it's true that Purdue and Tokyo are far apart, I didn't mention to Schmishmitt that you could do a lot better for the choice of the third far flung point than Notre Dame. He must have been lying in the gutter when we covered spherical geometry.

"Think it's the work of a ring?" I asked.

"Cut the puns, Mangum. Algebraists are dying."

"All right, all right." I hated to stop, but truth was I had run dry anyway. There are only two decent puns in all of mathematics and I had already used them both.

"How did they die?"

"In each case, they wasted away. Over a period of a month. Just stopped eating. Nobody can explain why. All three passed away within a week of one another."

"Maybe they weren't hungry."

"We figured that much out, Mangum. Now the question is, why?"

"So, how do I fit in?"

"I called you because I know you've done work in algebra. I figure it's got to be an inside job. I want you to go to AlgebraFest, taking place next week at the University of Texas. I already got you on the bill."

"You mean I'm giving a talk?"

"Yeah. The title is "On the peelability of semi-subring modules". I figured that was vague enough that you could throw something together over the weekend".

"Thanks a lot," I replied.

My plans to spend the weekend alone with a hot conjecture were evaporating quickly.

"By the way," I asked, "what is peelability?"

"I don't know," said Schmishmitt. "Make something up."

A week later, I found myself milling around with 100 other mathematicians in front of a registration table in the lobby of RLM, the tallest mathematics building in Texas.

"Well, well, well. If it isn't Dirk Mangum, P.I. Now what would bring you to AlgebraFest? I doubt it's the muffins."

I looked into the bulging eyes of Hal Balony, a module guy from Springfield State.

"Hello, Balony. I haven't seen you since you announced a proof of the Retraction Conjecture and then retracted it a week later."

"Just like you, Mangum, to bring up the one mistake I ever made in my career, a mistake I made 15 years ago, and to ignore all of the revolutionary results I am responsible for since then."

If you mean the Balony subgroup, the Balony semi-simple ring, and the Balony semi-literate subalgebra, then yes, I have ignored them. And it doesn't seem to have caused me any harm. What a bunch of, of. . . malarkey."

Balony turned red in the face.

"You should talk Mangum. Peelability? What the hell is that?"

Now it was my turn to turn red in the face. Truth was I hadn't pinned the details of the talk down yet, and it was coming up at 3:00.

"You'll have to come to my talk, Balony, if you want to hear about peelability."

"Sure, Mangum. I'll come to your talk if you come to mine at 5:00.

I'll be introducing some amazing math, math like you've never seen before. It is truly addictive." He smiled the kind of smile that makes your skin want to crawl up your neck and hide under your hair.

"We'll see, Balony," I said. "I may need to wash my underwear. I only brought one pair."

I reached deep down into the basket of muffins and pulled out a bran muffin the color of a UPS truck. Taking a huge bite, I said "Deericious," spraying Balony with crumbs. Turning quickly, I walked away. As soon as I made the corner, I disgorged the inedible mass into a ficus tree planter.

I spent the next hour in the library working on a definition for peelability. Then I wandered in on a few desultory talks, but you could find more excitement at a grading session for the final exam of a large lecture remedial course. Truth was that nobody at the conference had the mathematical chops that the dead algebraists had had, and the future of algebra was looking pretty bleak.

A few minutes before 3:00, I found my way to the lecture hall. It was surprisingly full. As I walked down to the podium, I heard a buzz. Several audience members pointed to me. The chair of the session stood up.

"Well, I know you are all excited to hear about this new concept of peelability. I will turn the podium over to Professor Mangum, who will explain it to us all."

I stepped up to the podium. Sitting in the front row was Hal Balony, wearing a dismissive sneer. An expectant silence fell over the lecture hall.

I looked down at the podium, grasping it with my hands, letting the tension rise, letting it go on much longer than they expected. Then, when they could hardly stand it another moment, I looked up and said,

"1946. A cramped office on the Princeton campus. A nondescript mathematician sits in his office day after day, night after night, disregarding his young wife and child at home (pause), a conjecture, a big conjecture, tantalizingly close. So close he could feel its breath on his neck. He was on the verge of one of the great discoveries of mathematics. But there was just one concept he couldn't grasp. One concept eluding his grasp."

"That young mathematician went on to become one of the most famous, if not the most famous mathematician of his generation, a name everyone in this room would recognize. . . . But did he figure out this concept? Did he ever solve the conjecture?"

"No, he did not. (Long pause.) Definition. Let G be a group. Let x be an element of G other than the identity. Let N be a normal subgroup of G that contains x, if such exists. Taking the quotient of G by N, x is trivialized. Yes, x is dead. Killed in the quotient process."

I looked out over the audience, hoping to see someone, anyone becoming flustered. But they all stared back at me, waiting expectantly.

"We think of the cosets of G/N as onion layers making up the onion that is the entire quotient group. This is the concept that the famous mathematician, whose name we need not utter, missed. That groups are merely certain types of onions, Vidalia, red, yellow. . . . Identifying the type of onion determines the group theoretic properties. And the x? We say the x is peelable."

I went on for another 40 minutes, but most of the audience lost interest once I got into my theory of groups as relish and other condiments.

After my talk, I slipped away to give Schmishmitt a call, and see if he had uncovered anything. He had.

"Listen, Magnum, do you know a Hal Balony?"

"I've had the pleasure," I said dryly.

"Well, get this. Balony was on leave at Purdue when Honeykey died. He was seen with Honeykey in his office right about the time Honeykey stopped eating. We think he might have poisoned Honeykey or somehow infected him with a virus. Maclaunders and Nakanimji received packages from Purdue shortly after this, probably sent by Balony. Keep an eye on him."

I had seen Balony slip into one of the seminar rooms after my talk, shutting the door behind him. I strolled casually down the hall, and quietly opened the door.

Balony was lecturing to the empty room, practicing his talk. He stopped when he heard me come in.

"Well, Mangum," he said. "I enjoyed the melodramatic aspects of your talk, but the content was on the meager side. It would have been nice if you proved something."

"It was a preliminary report, Balony. But I'm not here to discuss my talk. I'm here to talk about Honeykey."

"What's to talk about? He stopped eating, and now he's dead. That's what happens when you don't eat. End of story."

I grabbed Balony by the collar.

"Story's not over, Balony. You poisoned him, didn't you?"

Balony snorted, as he knocked my hands away.

"That is funny," he said. "The great Dirk Mangum. The hotshot from UCLA with his big fat NSF grant. You call yourself a P.I., and you don't have any idea what is going on."

"All right then, Balony. Why don't you tell me what is going on? I know you were at Purdue when Honeykey stopped eating. I know you mailed a package to each of Nakanimji and Maclaunders and they stopped eating after getting the packages. Some kind of virus, I suspect."

"A virus? Oh, that's good Magnum. It is a virus, but not the kind of virus you're thinking of."

"As confessions go, that's good enough for me," I said. "You can bore the cops with the details. Let's go, Balony."

"Wait a second, Mangum." He flipped on the projector. "Do you know Gauss's Last Lemma?"

Who didn't? Biggest open problem in the world.

"Here it is. And look here. We have all the pieces to the puzzle right in front of us."

I looked at the set of equations. Amazingly enough, it appeared he was right. There was the solution to the Kleinhold issue, which had dogged potential proofs up to now. And there was an end-run around the uncountability of the necessary axioms. An axiom that assumed them all away. It was amazing. This might actually lead to a solution to the entire problem.

I stared in disbelief. Balony laughed from what seemed a great distance.

I sat down to ponder the implications. It seemed like the solution was unbelievably close. I quickly began to make mental calculations. If the Toeplitz operator was semi-sufficient, then conjugating the commutator by a self-adjoint orthonormal pseudo-canonical basis would do the trick. Could it be? Could this be the solution of the greatest problem in the history of mathematics? Everything around me faded in importance. I felt an incredible need to finish it off. . . .

"And now, I would like to present Professor Hal Balony, who will tell us about his latest work."

Balony stood at the podium.

"2005," he said. "A small office at Springfield State. An earnest researcher working late into the night. He stumbles across something. Something very big. He finds himself inches away from a theorem like no other in the history of mathematics (pause). What theorem was that? How did he almost prove it? Feast your eyes on this!"

As he flipped on the projector, I rushed into the room.

"Don't look," I yelled. "Don't look at it."

Of course, this caused everyone in the room to look at Balony's slide. The result was almost instantaneous. Jaws slackened as their minds turned to contemplating the tantalizingly close result.

"Too late, Mangum," said Balony, a malevolent grin stretched across his face. "They've seen it."

I sprinted down the aisle, leaped onto the stage, and ripped the overhead cord out of the wall socket. The screen darkened immediately.

But as I looked out over the audience, I could see I was too late. Everyone was lost in thought, sinking deeper into the abyss. Balony sneered at me.

"You blew it, Mangum. Now it's only a matter of time before they starve to death, too wrapped up in the attempted solution to remember to eat."

"But I have to admit, I'm a bit surprised to see you here. Why aren't you trying to solve it? Are you immune? Is your mind too small to grasp the full implications? Too slow to realize how close it is? It only kills the better mathematicians, you know, leaving room for the rest of us. Lucky for you. Funny, isn't it? You're just like me."

"No, Balony, I'm nothing like you. I'm like the rest of them. I couldn't stop thinking about it."

"Then how is it you're not paralyzed like everyone else? How is it you are here?"

"Because, Balony, I solved it."

"No way," said Balony, a look of horrified disbelief on his face. "If Honeykey, Nakanimji, and Maclaunders couldn't solve it, then how could you?"

"Funny thing, Balony. Sometimes, just once in a while, luck plays a role in the math biz. In this case, turned out that there was one simple piece of the puzzle that those other mathematicians didn't have. One little idea."

"What's that?," asked Balony.

"It's called peelability," I said as I plugged the projector back in. I put a clean overhead slide on the glass, and then I started writing. Slowly, the members of the audience began to turn their attention to what I was doing. I set up the equations necessary and then I wrote down the punch line. There was an audible sigh. For some of these mathematicians, this was the closest they would ever get to orgasm.

Balony collapsed onto a chair, stunned by what had just transpired.

"Okay, Balony, now let's hear the rest of your story. Where did you get the idea? I don't believe for a second it was yours."

Baloney cradled his head in his hands.

"Honeykey must have found it," he said dully. "I went to see him at his office one day. He never did like talking math with me. Considered it a waste of his time. His door was open and there he was sitting at his desk in what appeared to be almost a trance. He could hear me, but clearly his thoughts were far, far away."

"I looked down on the desk in front of him and saw what he was thinking about, an outline of a possible proof of Gauss's Last Lemma. I scooped it up since he wasn't about to notice. Went back to my office and read it, but it didn't do anything to me. I could see what it was, but it didn't look that close to me."

"After a couple of days, I could see what was happening to Honeykey. He was fading away, losing contact with the real world. Couldn't eat. Couldn't sleep. It was obvious he wouldn't last long. That's when I sent copies to Nakanimji and Maclaunders."

"Why did you do that?"

"Do you have any idea, Mangum, what it's like to be a second-rate mathematician? To never get grants? To prove theorems that everyone ignores? Do you? No, you don't."

"I always wanted to be the best algebraist in the world. I tried working hard to get there, spending every waking moment on mathematics. But after a while, it became apparent that that wasn't going to do the trick. That left only one other option. Eliminate all the algebraists that were better than me. And if you hadn't interfered,

I would have succeeded. I would have been the greatest living algebraist in the world!"

"What a bunch of...of hooey, Balony. You amaze me with your naivete. Don't you think the rest of the world would have said, 'yes, he's the greatest living algebraist, but only because all the other algebraists died.' What kind of recognition is that?"

"It would have been good enough for me, Mangum. Good enough for me."

Balony was booked on charges of murder, attempted murder, and using an overhead projector as a dangerous weapon. He's at the type of educational institution that takes 20 years to graduate from, 15 with good behavior.

And Gauss's Last Lemma? Ultimately, it turned out there was an error in one of the propositions that was utilized to construct the proof, a twenty-year-old result first published by...you guessed it...Hal Balony. I believe that the reason Balony was unaffected by the proposed proof was that he knew, either consciously or unconsciously, that his result, upon which it was built, was in error.

So Gauss's Last Lemma is still out there. Like a black hole that can suck you in. It's still open. It's still waiting. But be very careful. It can be addicting.

A Subprime Lending Market Primer

You have probably heard quite a bit about the subprime lending market by now. But basic questions still remain. What is it? Why is everyone talking about it? How can I get in on the action?

These are all good questions. In order to clear up the confusion associated with these financial instruments, we will take this opportunity to answer these and other frequently asked questions.

What is a subprime?

Of course, everyone has heard of the primes. These are the integers with no nontrivial divisors. They include $2, 3, 5, 7, 11, \ldots$. Mathematicians have spent hundreds of years studying their properties. How many are there? What is their distribution? How come 2 is the only even one?

But what is a subprime?

A subprime is a prime number that is a factor of a larger prime. For instance, 7 is a factor of 851, making 7 a subprime. Subprimes are the building blocks of the prime numbers. And the prime numbers are the building blocks of the integers, which are themselves the building blocks of the real numbers, upon which all of mathematics is based. So, clearly subprimes play a critical role in any and all numerical computations, whether they be elementary additions or complex hyperextended equational manipulations.

But then, what does it mean to lend or borrow a subprime?

Subprimes are not as ubiquitous as one might first suppose. Considering all integers up to 1,000,000, there are fewer than 10,000 subprimes currently known, not nearly enough to go around. And once a subprime has been discovered, it is patented, and its use is restricted to the patent holder. An individual or corporation that uses the subprime without permission is subject to litigation and severe financial penalties.

Luckily, a lucrative market in subprime lending has developed. One can purchase the right to use a particular subprime for a specified time period through a variety of brokerage houses, including Bear Stearns and others.

What does this have to do with housing?

Yes, you have probably heard the word "housing" associated with the subprime lending market. Probably also "mortgage" and perhaps even "mess". Let's tackle each of these terms in turn.

First "housing". When a number is a subprime other than 2 or 3, its neighboring numbers cannot be subprimes. For example, although 7 divides 851, it's neighbors 6 and 8 do not. More generally, if n divides m where n and m are primes, then $n-1$ and $n+1$ cannot.

Let's prove this fact. This is something mathematicians do. They prove a fact in an irrefutable manner, so that there can be no question about its veracity.

We'll show that $n - 1$ does not divide m. A similar argument applies to $n+1$. We argue by contradiction. Thus, suppose that both n and $n-1$ divide m. First note that the $n-1$ and n cannot have a common nontrivial factor. For if k divided both $n-1$ and n, then k would divide their difference $n - (n-1) = 1$. Hence k must equal 1.

But if each of $n-1$ and n divides m, and they have no common nontrivial factors, then their product $(n-1)n$ must also divide m. This contradicts the fact m is a prime.

Of course, you might say, "Wait a minute. I agree that $n-1$ and $n+1$ cannot divide m, but they might divide some completely different prime." Good point. Didn't think you would notice that.

But it's not a problem. Because remember, n is a prime. And so unless $n=2$, n is an odd number. This means that for $n > 3$, $n-1$ and $n+1$ have to be even and greater than 2. So they cannot be primes. So they cannot be subprimes. Problem solved!

We call these neighboring numbers the *housing* for the given subprime. They play a similar role to that played by the housing for an electrical conduit, serving as a protective layer that keeps out weather and rodents. Often, when one leases a subprime, one also leases the housing to go with it.

And what about the "mortgage"?

The term "mortgage" traditionally refers to a contractual agreement to borrow money for the purchase of a domicile or other piece of real estate. The so-called *collateral* is the building or property itself.

In the case of the subprime market, there is no real estate. There is simply a number, together with its "house". But by abuse of terminology, the act of borrowing the money to purchase a lease on a subprime and its house has become known as a mortgage. These mortgages are a means to dramatically increase your investment potential. Instead of being limited to the funds you have on hand, you can "mortgage your future" and invest funds *that actually belong to someone else.*

And "mess"?

As you know, if you still own a house, it doesn't take long for it to become a mess. The same holds true for these number houses. A lease not only provides the rights to $n-1$, n, and $n+1$, it also provides the rights to *all* the real numbers in between. That is an *uncountable* collection of numbers. Many of them are given by nonrepeating decimals that *GO ON FOREVER*. If this collection of numbers gets just a little bit out of order, so, you can imagine the mess that ensues.

But don't worry. Things are not as bad as they first appear. For it turns out that the real numbers are *well ordered.* This means that there is a choice of ordering on the numbers such that ANY subset has a least element. It's not the usual ordering, but so what? If your real numbers get mixed up, just apply this ordering, and find the least element in the entire set. Then remove this element, and repeat the process. In no time at all, you will have your house in order.

Is there any risk?

Getting out of bed every morning is a risk. But if you stay in bed, you end up covered in bed sores. Not to mention a meteor smashing through your bedroom ceiling, and off you go to join the dinosaurs.

So yes, there is some risk. But keep in mind that these instruments are trusted by brokerage houses that are the bedrock of the entire financial community. If they feel safe and protected, why shouldn't you?

I'm still a little confused about what I do with a subprime once I lease it.

That's not a question.

What do I do with a sub-prime once I lease it?

That's entirely up to you. It's your oyster. You get to decide. There are essentially no restrictions. So go ahead, cut loose. Have some fun!

How do I sign up?

Legally, you cannot just send us your credit card information. We are supposed to send you a prospectus which you are then supposed to read. But the truth is that hardly anyone ever reads prospectuses, let alone using the plural of that word. Given the need for fast action, and the fact that you look smart, we can forgo the "information" stage. So don't wait. It's not clear how long this opportunity will remain available.

Fields Medalist Stripped

March 3, 2008: The International Congress of Mathematics announced today that they are stripping Wendell Holcomb of his Fields Medal after he tested positive for intelligence-enhancing drugs. Holcomb denied the charges. "Just because I never finished high school, and then solved the three-dimensional Poincaré Conjecture doesn't mean I took drugs."

When asked how he even knew about the problem, he said, "Nobody told me about it. I just got to thinking. There is a sphere that sits in 3-space, so there must be an analog one dimension up, which I called the 3-sphere. But could a different 3-dimensional space resemble this one in the sense that loops shrink to points, it has no boundary, and it's compact? Or is the 3-sphere the only 3-dimensional object that has those properties? Seemed like a reasonable question at the time."

Unaware that the conjecture was originally made by Henri Poincaré 100 years ago, Holcomb quickly proved it was true, scooping generations of mathematicians. He received the Fields Medal in mathematics for his efforts.

Residual amounts of Mentalicid were found in urine samples taken at Princeton University, where Holcomb is now the Andrew Wiles Professor of Mathematics.

"I never gave them urine samples," protested Holcomb.

Sargeant Karen Lagunda of the Princeton Police Department explained. "We have been testing the waste water coming out of the academic buildings for three years now, with the tacit cooperation of the administration. But Holcomb had been hoofing it over to the Seven Eleven and using the facilities there to avoid detection. Ultimately he had one too many slushies and couldn't wait 'til he got off campus."

"This would explain why he couldn't multiply two fractions on some days, and on others, he would solve conjectures that had been open for 50 years," said the department chair.

The revelations have thrown the mathematical world into chaos. Caffeine has long been used to enhance intellectual alertness. It is acknowledged that without coffee, mathematical productivity would have been half of what it was. But the new class of beta-enhancers that stimulate the transfer of impulses across neurons are in another class altogether.

"These drugs do turn you into a brainiac, no doubt about it," said Carolyn Mischner of the Harvard Medical School, "but they also have a variety of side effects, including seeing double, causing people to drive on the left side of the road, and the eventual degradation of the intellect when the drug is not in use. This causes users to stay on the drug for longer and longer periods. Eventually, the intellect is so diminished that the drug brings one back up to a functional level only, and then not even that."

Holcomb plans to appeal the decision. "This is so unfair. I think my pants are on backward."

The committees for the Nobel prizes in Economics and Medicine have not yet decided whether to strip Holcomb of his prizes in those fields as well.

More from the Mathematical Ethicist

Dear Dr. Brad,

I spent every Saturday night of the last nine years building a proof of the Ichihara-Warner Conjecture, the greatest outstanding question in Combinatorial Logic. The resulting paper has been honed and perfected and was ready to go out to the *Annals of Mathematics* where it most assuredly would have been accepted, when my 14-year old nephew happened to pick it up off my coffee table. He pointed out that one of the inequalities in a later lemma was obviously backward. This tiny defect has the effect of destroying my life's work. Now the entire problem boils down to a single inequality sign, which easily could point the other direction. It is highly unlikely that anyone would notice the problem. Chances are the referee will either be Ichihara or Warner. Ichihara himself often has his inequalities backward, and Warner dropped out of math and owns a car wash in Indiana somewhere. So, don't you think, just this once, I could ignore this tiny little error, and go ahead and publish the result? The nephew is no longer a problem.

Aaron Alkanacia

University of Northampton

Dear Aaron,

Unfortunately, the truth of the matter is that the bigger the result, the more carefully it is combed for errors. If this were some minor conjecture, there is a good chance you would get away with it. But Ichihara-Warner? The greatest conjecture in Combinatorial Logic? I don't think so. Graduate students from around the world would be studying your paper in seminars that would spring up overnight. One of them would be presenting it and would get into trouble over this lemma. Everyone in the seminar would make fun of him, giggling over his ineptitude, assuming the error was on his part, not on the author of this famous paper in the *Annals*. Then they would slowly come to realize where the error lay. One person after another would stop tittering until finally the entire seminar room would be bathed in cold stony silence. A year later, you would be living in the street, scraping by on pennies earned as a tutor for students who confuse 6's and 9's.

The sad truth, my dear friend, is that you cannot publish this work as the solution of the Ichihara-Warner Conjecture. No, you must find an obscure conjecture, preferably in an unrelated field, and publish your work as the solution to that conjecture instead. Then you can sleep easily, knowing that no one will ever bother to check the details of a conjecture that no one cares about in the first place. Good luck!

Dr. Brad

Dear Dr. Brad,

I have a student who was forced to miss the midterm because of the death of his grandmother. I always let students out of an exam in cases such as these, but for this particular student, this is the third time it has happened. What should I do?

Eleanor Oxentable

Southsoutheastern University

Dear Eleanor,

The likelihood that this student has three grandmothers, all of whom died this semester, is extremely low. Most likely, he is lying about the deaths of his grandmothers to avoid taking the exams. Of course, as mathematicians, we know that being extremely unlikely does not rule out the possibility that it could happen. If the parents have divorced and remarried, it could even be the case that he has four grandmothers, the fourth of whom will kick the bucket right before the final. In fact, it is not unheard of for elderly relatives to intentionally time their deaths so as to aid a granddaughter or grandson floundering in a math course. This phenomenon has been studied in the psychology literature. (See "The Final Exam: More Final Than We Thought?," *Psychology Today* (2004) 321-342, and "The Evolutionary Advantage of Extended Family Morbidity During Times of Crisis," *Misbehavioral Digest* (2005) 222-223.) There is at least one case where an entire extended Turkish family died, all of different causes, within three days of the son's final. Ironically, he chose to take the exam anyway, and did surprisingly well. It was obvious that his family had underestimated his abilities.

Given that there is some probability that your student is telling the truth and three of his grandmothers did die, it is incumbent upon you to be sympathetic. Think how you would feel. Give the kid a break.

Dr. Brad

Dear Dr. Brad,

How do you become a math ethicist? What's it like? Would I like it?

Carson Braintree

Age 10

Dear Carson,

Technically, I shouldn't address your questions, as they are not about mathematical ethics but instead, about a mathematical ethicist. However, since you are just a kid, and since I believe my readership is at least as interested in these questions as you are, I will indulge you.

I did not choose mathematical ethics as a profession. It chose me. From a very early age, I found myself in a variety of dilemmas of a mathematically moral nature. While still a toddler, I claimed I was a year older than I was by keeping track of the year of life I was in rather than the number of years already completed. Other children were upset by the advantage this provided me, and the resulting altercations were often settled on the playground rather than in scholarly debate.

Since then, I have continued to confront ethical dilemmas of a mathematical nature on an almost daily basis. When I receive incorrect change, should I point out the error? Should it matter if the error is in my favor? Should it matter if the error is in my favor and is in the amount of $3,407.45?

Over time, I came to realize I had considered these issues much more deeply than most. It seemed entirely appropriate that I share my knowledge.

And what is it like to be a mathematical ethicist? It is amazing. Thousands of mathematicians around the world rely on me to be their moral compass. A word here or there by me can make or break a career. Lives hang in the balance. It is an awesome responsibility, but a responsibility I take on willingly, and even relish. Having that kind of power is a rush.

Would you like it? That's like asking me if you like french fries at McDonald's. I don't know you, so how could I possibly know whether or not you would like it. But speaking probabilistically, as with the french fries, almost certainly you would. It is just that cool.

Dr. Brad

And here is a special private response to AR at UT with regard to the case of TD: Ixnay on the enuretay.

Well, here we are again at the end of our time together. I hope you have found this column as ethically inspiring to read as I have found it to write. And remember, numbers don't lie, people do. Keep those letters coming! See you next time!

Math Fall Fashion Preview

Characters

Arturo Vincense

Katherine Delavoise

Arthur: Good evening. I am Arturo Vincense, Italian fashion critic for the La Taurus.

Katherine: And I am Katherine Delavoise, reporter on the style desk for Vogue. We're very excited to be hosting one of the most important events of the season. Yes, we're at the Mathematics Fall Fashion Preview. We will be seeing the hottest new clothes from the epicenters of mathematical fashion. This is an event of Gaussian significance. Are you expecting some surprises, Arturo?

Arturo: Oh, yes. I certainly hope so. I love a good surprise.

Katherine: Look, Arturo, here comes the first department. I see from the program this must be Harvard University.

Arturo: Yes, Katherine. This is a department that does not take risks. Goes with the classics.

Katherine: Oh, yes I see. The button-down white shirt with slacks or jeans. Oh, but look at the drape.

Arturo: Yes, they are having a love affair with the fabric.

Katherine: And I see the chair is wearing a neck tie.

Arturo: Yes, it is a statement. It says look, look I am in charge. He is not afraid to say, "I decide who teaches at 8:00 A.M." It's brash in that understated Harvard way.

Katherine: And look Arturo, here comes Berkeley.

Arturo: We should expect a few pairs of Birkenstocks here, a West Coast version of mathwear. But you will see them with athletic socks.

Katherine: Yes, and I see a t-shirt or two. The message is, "We are Berkeley. We do it our way."

Arturo: Yes. Notice they are from California but there isn't a tan in the bunch. It's work, work, work for them.

Katherine: Mathematical fashion has had its ups and downs over the years, hasn't it Arturo? Who can forget the plastic pocket protector craze of the early 60's. It was de rigeur at the time. And of course the short sleeved white button down that dominated the late 60's. Is there any single item that dominates the math scene these days?

Arturo: Not really, Katherine. Mathematicians are expressing themselves freely. They are saying I am an individual. I do sheaf cohomology and I am proud of it.

Katherine: I see. Some of them look quite unkempt.

Arturo: Yes, it is intentional. They want you to know, "I am not concerned enough with human society to comb my hair. My brain thinks only abstract thoughts." That sort of thing. Look Katherine, coming down the runway. It's the Princeton University Mathematics Department. Look at that strut. They know who they are, and they want you to know it too. This group is not afraid to be bold.

Katherine: Oh, I see what you mean Arturo. They walk with such confidence.

Arturo: Yes, this is what makes math fashion so influential. This is the only academic discipline where the individuals know they are right. They can even prove it. What would the fashion industry do without them?

Katherine: Look, some wide wale corduroys. If I'm not mistaken, they are brushed against the nap.

Arturo: Yes, Katherine, this is not your typical math department. They are willing to go out on a limb.

Katherine: Look at the pose the chair has struck. With his lips pouting. They are clearly enjoying themselves out there. And I see there are some sweaters returning with the fall. Moth holes are optional.

Arturo: And notice, Katherine, how the mathematicians are getting creative with the socks. I've already seen black, brown and white today, and one with navy on one foot, grey on the other. That is why mathematics remains the center of fashion sense today. It is that willingness to take risks.

Katherine: Yes, Arturo, it's a statement. I'm not sure what the statement is, but it's a statement.

Arturo: The only word that fits is impetuous.

Katherine: Arturo, how many of these outfits are off the rack and how many are created by name designers?

Arturo: Katherine, all of them are from designers. These ideas are so clever, the details so subtle. Only someone with a sublime eye could possibly pull these elements together.

Katherine: Do you mean Calvin Klein, Ralph Lauren, or Bill Blass?

Arturo: No, I mean Felix Klein, Pierre Laurent, and Hyman Bass.

Katherine: Oh, here comes Oberwolfach, mathwear with a German slant. There's more in the way of woolens. Look how they come down the runway, as if they are just learning to walk. Perhaps they have been stuffed in tiny seminar rooms all day.

Arturo: Or at least that is what they would like you to believe, Katherine. Oh, look, that seam there, ripped under the arm. This is incredible. And see how she pretends not to know the tear is there. Her head is in a cloud.

Katherine: Arturo, there seems to be a swing away from the sneakers that so dominated the mathematical footwear of the 80's. It's a return to leather, brown or black.

Arturo: Yes, Katherine. To quote Felix Brouwder, "The baby boomers have finally grown up. They want to look like Hilbert."

Katherine: And here is Cambridge University. No academic robes?

Arturo: No it's a studied casual look for the Fall. A look that says, "To hell with ceremony, we have great theorems."

Katherine: There, look, is that a dress?

Arturo: Yes, young women are rebelling against the obligatory jeans and slacks that were standard wear for women in mathematics for 20 years. They are saying, "We prove our own theorems, we can wear our own clothes."

Katherine: Now what about mathematical sleepwear? What's the latest there?

Arturo: We have seen a movement away from pajamas and onesies to the t-shirt, usually ratty and often with a mathematical theme printed on it, such as a conference announcement or a fractal picture. This is normally worn with jockies or boxers.

Katherine: Am I mistaken or is there a lot of facial hair on the male algebraic topologists?

Arturo: No Katherine, you are exactly right. The male algebraic topologists relish the opportunity to stroke a beard as they contemplate spectral sequences.

Katherine: And here is the Institute for Advanced Study. Note the dark colors. They are researchers, not teachers, so they needn't worry about chalk dust ruining a look. Can I ask you? What keeps their pants up? Those slacks are hanging so low on the waist. It seems a miracle.

Arturo: They must pin them up from the inside before the show. But how ingenius it is. As if they needn't abide by any laws, including gravity.

Katherine: Look, there is an oversized calculator hanging from that belt there.

Arturo: Katherine, it is a retro statement, a return to the '70's. How exquisite.

Katherine: Arturo, otherwise, I haven't noticed much in the way of accessories today. Why is that?

Arturo: Well, Katherine, mathematicians learn to be concise in their writing. That is reflected in their style. They tend not to embellish. Clean lines, monochromatic fabrics. They are taking their cue from the post-modern industrial minimalism, which itself grew out of the Arts and Crafts furniture movement at the turn of the century. But it has a distinctly mathematical twist.

Katherine: Well, I see the show is coming to an end. The audience is on its feet, whistling and clapping vigorously. We should see the impact from Milan to Göttingen. I want to thank you, Arturo, for joining us today at what was one of the most exciting events of the Fall, sure to keep us buzzing for months to come. For all of you watching, stay tuned for a special about the Baker's Transformation on the *Cooking with Bob Devaney Show*, as we continue round-the-clock broadcasting at the Math Channel. Thanks for tuning in. (*Waves goodbye.*)

Dr. Yeckel and
Mr. Hide

"Oh, what a shame, what a shame." Inspector Armand looked down at the now still form of Dr. Yeckel. "Such a waste."

"But Inspector," said Sargeant Lonigan with horror. "That man lying there looks different than when he collapsed just now. He has transformed into someone else while he was lying there. I am sure of it."

"Ah, Lonigan, in a sense he is the same man and in a sense he is not."

"Yer speaking nonsense there, Inspector."

"Well, then sit down here Lonigan, and I will tell you a tale. A tale that will make your blood run colder than the Thames in January."

"It's not one of those math stories of yours, is it Inspector?"

"In fact, it tis, indeed. A story that will make your teeth chatter like a squirrel in heat."

"Fire away, Inspector. My teeth need a good chatter."

"This story begins with a young instructor of mathematics, name of Dr. Yeckel. A new Ph.D., he was bright, friendly, and well scrubbed.

Students loved him. Had a job at the university there in town. Taught calculus mostly and sometimes linear algebra."

"Oh, I've heard linear algebra is quite the course."

"Yes, Lonigan, it is, it certainly is. Now this Dr. Yeckel, he enjoyed teaching. He liked the sound of chalk on a board, the rustle of students in their seats, the smell of lysol in the bathrooms. He especially liked that smell.

"And the students knew he liked it. Teaching, that is. And they appreciated the attention he showered on them. His willingness to meet with them at odd hours, to answer their emails and to help them with the problems. He liked them and they liked him. Yes, he was happy as a mongoose in a snake pit, he was. But you see, teaching was only part of his job there at the institution of higher learning. Because you see, that institution was what is called a research university. Do you know what that means Lonigan?"

"Errr, does that mean they do some kind of nasty experiments, Inspector?"

"Not exactly, Lonigan. It means they search for new truths. Sometimes with nasty experiments, and sometimes without.

"Now this Dr. Yeckel had specialized in an area called number theory. That is the study of numbers, like 2, 3, 5, and 7. When he was focussed on his teaching he was fine. But then he would get involved in his research. And suddenly a transformation would overcome him."

"You mean he would become a creature."

"Exactly Lonigan. His hair would become unkempt. His fingernails would become dirty. His eyes would be bloodshot, and his shirt would become unacceptable in its odor."

"Oh, my goodness, Inspector, a creature. Was he dangerous?"

"You have no idea, Lonigan. He was in a deranged state of mind. The world as we know it meant nothing to him. He could easily step in front of a moving car without thinking to look if it was safe. His mind would be off on Diophantine Approximations, a very abstract area of mathematical consideration indeed."

"Sounds fancy."

"Oh, believe me, it tis. And he was hooked on the Stillwell Conjecture."

"Is that some kind of hard math problem?"

"Only the greatest open conjecture in all of Diophantine Approximation is all. He became obsessed with it. Suddenly, his students weren't so important to him. He would forget to meet his classes. The students that had loved him so much would sit waiting for him hour after hour, but he would not come. And when he did come, it was even worse. They hardly recognized him. They would ask him a question, with their bright eyes and inquisitive minds, and he would say, "Hmmm?" and lean against the wall lost in thought. They would purposely make extra-loud rustling sounds, but he could not hear them. Sometimes, he would drop the chalk in mid-lecture and wander out of the room. The poor students, their little hearts were broken."

"A sad tale indeed, Inspector."

"Sometimes we don't know what we have until it is gone, Lonigan. Such is how it was with him. Eventually, his enrollments dropped. His wife left him, his dog ran away, and the university threatened to fire him if he didn't meet his classes."

"As it should be."

"Perhaps so. But then, Lonigan, as often happens in life, fate provided a sudden and unexpected twist."

"How so, Inspector?"

"Yeckel showed that the Stillwell Conjecture was equivalent to Q equals NQ."

"Yer talking gibberish Inspector. I'm no mathematician. I just walk a beat."

"Leave it to say, Lonigan, that he had made a major step toward the solution of the Stillwell Conjecture. Suddenly he was a mathematical celebrity. He was invited to speak at colleges and universities all over the country. Receptions were thrown in his honor, with sparkling cider and little stuffed mushrooms. He received large federal grants to continue his research and the university received the overhead on the grants. Of course, all was forgiven, and he was given tenure."

"Doesn't that mean they cannot fire him for as long as he lives?"

"It does, indeed, Lonigan, it does indeed. And now the problem got worse. His hair and beard grew longer and more tangled. The t-shirt he wore began to come apart at the arm pits. His pants were frayed and stained up and down with coffee."

"Did the university take action?"

"Oh, yes, they did. They made him chair of the Mathematics Department."

"Now why did they do that?"

"Well, he was the most successful mathematician in the department."

"And what does that have to do with running a department?"

"Ah, Lonigan, now you have whacked the nail on its tiny top. It needn't have anything to do with running a department. And in this case, it did not. Yeckel continued to work on his research to the exclusion of all his other duties. Appointments were missed. Staffing reports were not submitted. Hires were not made. Within a year's time, the Mathematics Department was in a shambles."

"Well, Inspector, then the university must have realized its mistake."

"But Lonigan, you must remember, universities are not like individuals with common sense and the ability to act on it. No, they are more like a thousand toads trapped in a Bentley, all hopping this way and that, slapping against the windows and muddying the plush leather interior."

"Oh, I see."

"So the university left him in charge. And the department finally revolted. Whole subdisciplines jumped ship. By the end of his term, there was no one left but the lifers who couldn't get work elsewhere."

"And is that what did him in, Inspector?"

"No, Lonigan, no. He could have cared less what happened to the rest of the department. All that mattered to him was his research. But then he opened the paper one morning to find that $Q = NQ$ had been proved by a graduate student from Southhampton. This immediately implied the Stillwell Conjecture. It was too much for him to bear. His mathematical heart broke."

"Ah. I see."

"He collapsed on the spot. This spot right before us. And since his dream of proving the Stillwell Conjecture had been destroyed, his body reverted to its former state. He was no longer the driven intellectual who derived all his meaning from the pursuit of knowledge, ignoring the real world around him. Now he reverted to the man he had been, the nurturing caring teacher that the students had loved so much."

"Ah, but it was too late, Inspector."

"Hardly. Nothing a good bath, a haircut, and a breath mint can't fix. Help him up Lonigan. He should be fine in an hour or so."

The Pepsi Putnam Challenge

"Ladies and gentlemen. Welcome to the Nabisco Amphitheater and the ceremonies to honor the top contenders in the Pepsi Putnam Challenge. We are pleased to have Karen Parton, *Nike's* director of marketing, who will emcee today's festivities."

"Thanks, Bill. What a thrill it is to be here today with these future professional matheletes. I am so glad that *Nike* can contribute in its small way to these intellectual giants. Knowing that their *Nike* footwear was gripping the floor, that their *Nike* warm-up jackets prevented them from getting a chill and that their *Nike* superabsorbent athleticwear soaked up their sweat as they pored over these difficult problems; well, it just makes me proud."

"I am now pleased to present to you the *Nestle's Crunch* Professor of Mathematics from Harvard University, Cranston Lamont, who will say a few words."

"Thank you, Karen. And thanks to the innumerable corporations, who through their sponsorship, make this event possible. Special mention goes to American Airlines for flying these math students out here for the ceremony and giving them plenty of Pepsi along the way to keep up their caffeine levels. And thanks to American Express for providing them with AMEX cards to pay for the necessary incidentals like erasers, pencils, and pads. Let American Express take care of you. MCI long distance is proud to have contributed cellular phones so students could contact their coaches back home. The calling plan reverts to the standard one after today. Internet access has been provided by America Online available to the students through the SGI workstations provided by Silicon Graphics."

"Thanks a lot, Cranston, for filling us in on which corporations have made this competition possible. Now, as you all know, the Pepsi Putnam Challenge pairs talented math students with celebrity teammates as they take the Putnam Exam, which consists of a set of twelve formidable math problems. Let me introduce some of the contestants."

"Here is the Pennzoil Team, Anant Lerosky from Harvard University and his teammate John Tesh. Anant, did you find John helpful?"

"Actually, he kind of made me nervous, sitting there looking over my shoulder."

"And John, how did you find it?"

"Oh, it was very exciting. We worked together. Anant figured out the problems and wrote up the solutions. Then I rewrote them to look nicer and added some doodles. When it looked like Anant's energy was flagging, I sang a few tunes from my upcoming CD, 'Songs for Seagulls'."

"Yes we are all looking forward to that. And here we have the Kellogg's Pop Tart Team, Kathy Panaur of MIT competing with Richard Simmons. Kathy, how much help was Richard on the math portion of the exam?"

"He didn't show up."

"Ha ha, Richard didn't show up. What a cut up. How did you feel while you were taking the exam?"

"I guess I wish that the camera guy could have stopped shoving that camera in my face. It made it hard to concentrate."

"Yes, well, Kathy, without that cameraman, this would just be a bunch of people taking a test, now wouldn't it?"

"And here is Jeff Terwilliger from the University of Waterloo competing with Ed McMahon on the Kitchenaid Appliances for the Home Team. I'm sure you audience members remember the slow-mo of Jeff's pencil point breaking on Problem 7. How did you feel when that happened, Jeff?"

"What do you mean? I just picked up another pencil."

"Yes, we saw the replay. Besides that near disaster, how do you think you did?"

"Well, I would have done okay, but Ed kept bumping me with that giant cardboard check. Why does he always carry that thing around?"

"Nobody knows, Jeff. How did you like the half-time show?"

"I would have preferred spending the time boning up on my integration tricks, but that's hard when they're shooting live animals out of cannons."

"I liked that part, too. But now, it's the moment we have all been waiting for. It's time to find out who has won the Pepsi Putnam Challenge. Here are the results tabulated by the Mathematics Department of the University of California at Berkeley. They have an 800 number if you are interested in graduate school."

"I'll just open the envelope provided by Office Max. Well, what do you know? I am thrilled to announce that this year's winner is the Kellogg's Pop Tart Team of Kathy Panaur and Richard Simmons. Congratulations, Kathy. This means a full fellowship to study mathematics at Harvard, a lifetime supply of Rayovac batteries, and a lucrative endorsement contract with Fischer Toys. What would you like to say to the young matheletes in our audience who would aspire to be as successful as you?"

"Well, I guess I would just say that it is important to work lots of problems, and study the past exams."

"And when you are studying, what station do you have your TV tuned to?"

"What do you mean? I can't study with the TV on."

"Ha, ha, very funny. Now come on, Kathy, tell them what station you watch as you study, with call letters the first three letters of the alphabet."

"Oh, yes, I watch ABC television, where I'm part of their family."

"That's right. And what do you eat while you are studying?"

"I like to eat Kellogg's Frosted Sparkly Pop Tarts, the ones that glow in the dark."

"Thanks, Kathy, for those precious words of wisdom. Well, that wraps it up for us today. Stay tuned to ESPN for the Frito-Lay Nobel Prize chicken fights. We'll have the finals between Economics and the Peace Prize Winners. You won't want to miss it. We will see you all next year, when mathematics and corporate sponsorship again join hands to present to you the Pepsi Putnam Challenge."

(Cut to Commercial.)

Vital Sines

Cast:

Intercom

Theorem

Grad student

Resident 1

Resident 2

Vinson

Waldhaugen

Nazur

("Vital Sines" title on overhead, lights down low. Turn off the overhead.)

Intercom: Dr. Vinson, Dr. Vinson, you are needed in the operating room. We have an emergency.

(Lights come up on the operating room. There is the theorem covered in sheet on the table and two residents in lab coats. Also one grad student dressed normally. Vinson strides in wearing a lab coat.)

Vinson: Okay, fill me in. Who brought this theorem in?

Grad: I did.

Vinson: What are you, a grad student?

Grad: Yes. *(Looks down, slightly embarrassed.)*

Vinson: That's okay. It's nothing to be ashamed of. We were all grad students once. Now tell me. What happened?

Grad: It wasn't looking where it was going, stepped off the curb and pow *(slaps hands together)* took a counterexample straight in the kisser. It's a miracle it's breathing at all.

Vinson: "Okay, Dr. Silva. Give me a medium-sized lemma immediately. One of those extra-absorbent ones." *(Resident 1 hands paper to him. He uses it to patch a gaping wound in the side of the theorem.)* "Dr. Loepp, what's the blood pressure?"

Resident 2: Low and dropping, Doctor, it doesn't look good.

Vinson: Okay, give me three cc's of sheaf theory.

(Resident 1 does the injection.)

Resident 2: Blood pressure's stabilizing.

Vinson: *(To grad)* Is it your theorem?

Grad: Oh, gosh, no. It's Nazur's Theorem.

(Suddenly the emergency light on the monitor begins to flash.)

Resident 2: *(Urgently)* We're losing the patient, Doctor. No pulse.

Vinson: Stand back. Hand me the paddles. Give me 100 volts of algebraic K-theory. Clear! *(Resident 1 hands him the paddles. Vinson applies the paddles and the theorem bucks on the table.)*

Resident 2: Nothing.

Vinson: Again.
(Theorem bucks again.)

Resident 2: *(Gives a thumbs up sign.)* We have a pulse, Doctor. It's alive...for now.

(Vinson wipes the sweat off his brow with his sleeve.)

Vinson: Okay, we need Waldhaugen, now.

Resident 1: He's not going to like it. I saw him putting on a tie to head over to the administration building.

Vinson: I don't really give a damn. Have him paged.

(Resident 1 talks into phone and then we hear Intercom.)

Intercom: Dr. Waldhaugen, Dr. Waldhaugen, you are needed in the operating room.

Resident 2: What should we do in the meantime?

Vinson: It looks to me like we may have to do Dehn surgery. See if you can see a decent solid torus in there. We'll have to remove it and then sew it back in differently.

Resident 2: Have you ever done Dehn surgery before?

Vinson: What do I look like, a topologist? But what choice do I have? We are flying by the seat of our pants here.

(Waldhaugen strolls through the door, wearing lab coat, rubber gloves and tie.)

Waldhaugen: Vinson, I was just on my way to wheedle $200,000 out of the provost. This had better be good.

(Vinson nods toward the table.)

Vinson: This theorem is barely hanging on. I've done everything I can.

(Waldhaugen peremptorily looks it over.)

Waldhaugen: It's a goner. Off to see the provost. *(He starts to pull off his rubber gloves.)*

(Vinson grabs his shoulder and spins him around.)

Vinson: Hold it, Waldhaugen. You took an oath when you received your Ph.D. An oath to try to save every theorem that was wheeled through this door. You're not walking out of here without doing everything you can.

Waldhaugen: Still the idealist, huh, Vinson? If you had seen half the pathetic theorems I have seen over the years, stitched together out of laughable lemmas, riddled like Swiss cheese with inconsistencies, you'd know that sometimes you have to just let them go and move on. Some of them can't be saved. We're not gods here. We're just mathematicians.

Vinson: Yes, but as mathematicians, we have a duty to do the best we can.

Waldhaugen: What can I do? It's just another theorem.

Vinson: Well, actually, it's the department chair's theorem.

Waldhaugen: What? This is Nazur's Theorem? Why didn't you say so? You, get me a couple of low-dimensional corollaries, let's make it dimension 4, and you, I'm going to need some lemmas from number theory with big names on them, like Euler and Fermat. We may need to do a corollary bypass. Whose the differential geometer here?

Resident 1: *(Holding a paper)* That's me.

Waldhaugen: What are you doing with that conjecture? We're not writing an expository paper here, we're trying to save a theorem. I want you to look up everything you can find by do Carmo and bring it down here, stat. *(Resident 1 leaves.)* Vinson, you've always been good at algebra. See if you can stem the flow of logic out of that mess there where a group was confused with its quotient under a PSL(2) action.

(Waldhaugen pokes the theorem here and there, as he looks it over carefully.)

Waldhaugen: Look. I think we are going to need to do a transplant. Vinson, do you have any old theorems lying around?

Vinson: You're not gutting one of my theorems, Waldhaugen.

Waldhaugen: Okay, okay, let's get one from one of the junior faculty, preferably one that's up for tenure. They'll certainly give up a theorem to help the chair. Set it up, Vinson. I'm going to speak to Harry Nazur.

(Waldhaugen goes to the waiting room. While this occurs, others in the operating room continue to work on the theorem. The chair of the Mathematics Department sits bent over in the waiting room with his face in his hands, and his shoulders heaving. Waldhaugen walks over and puts a hand on his arm. Nazur leaps up.)

Nazur: "Waldhaugen, thank God you're here. What's going on in there? Is it going to be all right?" *(He starts to sob again. Waldhaugen puts his arm around the chair's shoulders.)*

Waldhaugen: It's okay, Harry, no need to cry. I have everything under control. If anyone can save that theorem, I can.

Nazur: Oh, please, save that theorem. I've already announced it. If it doesn't make it, I could become the laughingstock of the semi-simple Lie Algebra research community.

Waldhaugen: I'll do my best, Harry, but you know, work conditions in the department make it difficult for me. I really need a new Mac Pro with two 2.26 Gigahertz Quad-Core processors and 32 gigabytes of memory.

Nazur: Whatever you want, Waldhaugen, just save that theorem.

Waldhaugen: Don't worry. I will. *(He turns and goes back to the operating room. As he re-enters the operating room, he is grinning from ear to ear.)*

Vinson: Don't bother. It's gone.

Waldhaugen: What do you mean?

Vinson: While you were out there playing "Let's Make a Deal", the theorem had a logical coronary. There was nothing we could do.

(Waldhaugen rushes over to the table and looks down at the now still pile. He shakes his head sadly.)

Waldhaugen: *(To himself)* I can't believe it. I had a Sun Enterprise Ultra 2. *(He straightens and turns to face Vinson.)* Well, Vinson, I will hand it to you. Given the mess Nazur gave you to work with, you did well keeping it alive as long as you did.

Vinson: *(Laughs)* Was that a compliment?

Waldhaugen: You know, Vinson, if you weren't such a bleeding-heart mathematician, you could do well in this business. You need to relax, take up administration, and stop stitching up lemmas that'll never see the light of publication.

Vinson: And you, Waldhaugen, have lost sight of the very thing that drove you to be a mathematician in the first place. It wasn't for the glamor, the accolades, the talk shows. It couldn't have been, since there aren't any in mathematics. And it wasn't for the grants or the prizes. No, you did it for one reason and one reason only, for the beauty of mathematics. You did it out of love.

(Pause)

Intercom: Dr. Vinson, Dr. Vinson, you are needed in Emergency. We have a head-on collision between two contradictory theorems, and one of them is with corollary.

Vinson: I have to go.

Waldhaugen: *(Blocks him)* You don't have to go. Someone else can deal with the "crisis". Let's go over to administration and I'll introduce you to some deans. Maybe we could have some sherry.

(Vinson pushes Waldhaugen out of the way.)

Vinson: Waldhaugen, there is nothing I would enjoy less. *(He motions to the others in the room.)* Come with me. I'll need you.

(They leave Waldhaugen alone. He walks over to the operating table and leans over the now still theorem.)

Waldhaugen: *(To the theorem)* You know, pal, he's right. I was like that once. Ready to save the mathematical world. I loved it all. What happened to me? Where did I lose my drive? Was it filling out the travel vouchers? Writing grants for programs that didn't deserve support? Chairing the library committee? What made me give up the good fight? *(Shakes head sadly and shrugs)* Well, by now, they are probably out of cappucino at the Comptroller's Office. Maybe, I'll swing by emergency and see if Vinson needs any help. *(He flicks off the lights as he leaves.)*

Rumpled Stiltsken

Once upon a time there was a topologist who lived with his daughter in a tiny office in the Math Building at the University of Chicago. One day, the chairman of the department happened to stop to talk to a colleague just outside the door to the topologist's office.

"The hiring season look's tough," said the chairman, a bit discouraged. "I hope we can find someone extraordinary."

The topologist, who was barely known to the chair, stepped out of his office. "Pardon me, sir," he said timidly. "I hate to interrupt, but I know of an extraordinary mathematician. She can turn coffee into theorems."

"Really?" said the chair. "And who is that?"

"It is my daughter," said the topologist.

"Then send her to my office this afternoon," said the chair.

That afternoon, the topologist's daughter was ushered into the chair's office. She was quite apprehensive, as she had no idea how to turn coffee into theorems.

"Follow me," said the chair, as he led her to the department lounge.

"Here you see a coffee maker, and three pots of coffee. I want you to turn the three pots of coffee into theorems by morning. If you do not, then I will see to it that the only job you ever get is at a regional university with high research expectations and a teaching load of four courses per semester."

With that he left the lounge, locking the door behind him.

The poor girl was decimated. She fell sobbing on the couch. "Oh, what will I ever do?" she cried. "My career is over before it has even started."

Suddenly, as if by magic, the door to the lounge swung open and in walked a squat disheveled creature, with long matted beard and hair. He was dressed in a dirty t-shirt, jeans and an even dirtier red sports coat. He seemed surprised to see her.

"What are you doing here?" he asked. "Oh, the chair has said that I must turn this coffee into theorems, or he will destroy my career."

"And you don't know how to turn coffee into theorems?" asked the little man, a smile playing across his lips.

"Oh, no. I have no idea how. My father just said I could to impress the chair."

"And what will you give me if I turn this coffee into theorems?" said the unsanitary fellow.

"Ummm, how about this mint condition copy of Stewart's Calculus book?" she suggested, pulling the book from her briefcase.

"Let's see," he replied. "The new edition? I could get 50 bucks for that. You got a deal."

And with that, the strange man gulped down all three pots of coffee. His bloodshot eyes began to glow. His eyebrows started to twitch. Then he sat down before a pad of paper and wrote furiously for three hours. When he was done, the pages of three pads were covered with the most beautiful lemmas the girl had ever seen.

"That ought to do the trick," said the little man, and with that, he scooped up the calculus book and was gone.

The next morning the chair unlocked the door, expecting to find the girl crying or sleeping, with nothing to show for her night. But his jaw dropped open when he saw the scribblings on the pad. "This is some of the most original work I have ever seen," he said. "It is really quite good."

"Thank you," said the girl timidly. "Can I go now?"

"What, are you kidding? This is the beginning of some really good mathematics. But you need to fill in the details. Flesh out the theory. Come back this evening."

When the girl arrived that night, the chair pointed to six pots of coffee sitting on the table.

"If you don't turn this coffee into theorems, I will make sure the only work you get is as a recitation instructor, teaching fifteen problem sessions a week for large calculus lectures." And again, he locked her in the lounge.

The girl fell sobbing on the couch. But she said to herself, if the little man can do it, why can't I? With that she went over and poured herself a cup of the steaming brown liquid. She took a sip and spit it out immediately. "Ahhrgh," she said. "This tastes like it has been sitting in the pot for the last 12 hours." Which in fact it had.

But then the door swung open again, and in walked the little man. His jeans were torn at the knee and his teeth appeared to never have experienced the friction of a toothbrush.

"Back again, are we?" he said.

"Yes, the chair said I must turn these six pots of coffee into theorems by morning, or he will turn me into a recitation instructor."

"And what, pray tell, will you give me if I do it for you?"

The girl thought for a moment and then pointed to her computer briefcase.

"How about my laptop?" she asked hopefully.

She handed it to the man. "Hmmm, looks like a Mac Titanium Power PC G4, 800 MegaHertz, with one megabyte L3 and 256K L2 cache. You got a deal."

So again, he gulped down the coffee, and set to work. Six hours later, he had filled six pads of paper with theorems and proofs.

"This should do it," he said. And grabbing up the laptop, he disappeared out the door.

When the chair arrived the next morning, he was flabbergasted by the beauty of the mathematics on the pads.

"This is really good stuff," he said enthusiastically. "These are the germs for a whole new theory. I am really impressed."

"Good," said the girl nervously. "Now can I go?"

"Yes, but you must come back tonight," said the chair. "You have more work to do."

That evening, the chair sat her down before twelve pots of coffee.

"If you don't turn this coffee into theorems," he threatened, "I will make you into a permanent grader for our remedial algebra course. But if you do succeed, I will give you a tenure-track position on the faculty here at Chicago." Then he turned and left the lounge, locking the door behind him.

The girl fell on the couch sobbing. It was too much to hope the smelly man would be back to help her once more. And besides, she had nothing left to give him.

Suddenly the doorknob turned and in he walked.

"Still trying to turn coffee into theorems, are we? Haven't learned how to do it yet?"

"Oh, no," she said. "I can't do it. And the chair is going to make me into a permanent grader. Oh, woe is me."

"And what will you give me if I do it for you?" asked the hair-encumbered individual.

"I don't know," said the girl. "I don't have anything left to give."

The little man grinned mischieviously. "Oh, I think you do," he said. "I want you to give me your first-born theorem."

"What do you mean?" asked the girl.

"The first theorem that you prove yourself, I want you to give it to me, to claim as my own."

Now the topologist's daughter knew that if she said no, she wouldn't ever have the opportunity to create her own theorems anyway. So there wouldn't be anything to lose. On the other hand, if she did survive all this nonsense, and had a career as a mathematician, what was one theorem more or less? So she agreed. The little man laughed delightedly.

"Oh, yes, we have a bargain," he laughed as he danced about the room. Then he gulped down all twelve pots of coffee, and worked through the entire night, finishing just before daybreak.

"Remember our deal," he said as he slipped out the door, leaving twelve pads of paper filled with wondrous mathematics on the table.

When the chair arrived, he was stunned by the level of work that he saw.

"You have a job, a tenure track job," said the chair, shaking her hand enthusiastically.

So the young woman began her career at Chicago. She was an able teacher, and enjoyed that aspect of her job. But at first, she found it difficult to work on her research, as her other duties were so numerous.

But one day, she attended a number theory seminar. The speaker presented a discussion of Catalan's Conjecture, which says that the only two consecutive powers of whole numbers are the integers 8 and 9. She found the question quite fascinating. Soon, she was spending all her time working on the problem. She would have worked even more but sometimes exhaustion overcame her. Finally, one evening, wanting to continue her work but unable to keep her eyes open any longer, she stumbled into the department lounge and quickly swallowed a cup of coffee, before she had a chance to gag.

Suddenly, she felt awake. Within minutes, the caffeine was coursing through her system, and her neurons seemed to be firing every which way. She worked all that night and by morning, she had proved Catalan's Conjecture.

Although tired and in great need of sleep, she decided to wait until the chair arrived at 8:00 to tell him the good news. At 7:30, just as her eyes were closing with exhaustion, the door to her office swung open and the little man, whom she had not seen for the last two years, bounded in.

"I am here to collect my debt," he said.

"Oh, no," pleaded the assistant professor. "It's too good. You can have my next one."

"I don't want your next one," said the diminutive hairball. "I want this one."

"Please, please, don't take it. It has taken me all this time to learn how to turn coffee into theorems. I can't give it up."

"I'll tell you what," said the little man, an evil grin on his face. "If you can guess my name, I will not take your theorem. And I will give you three days to guess it." He laughed then and scooted out of the office.

The young woman thought to herself that this couldn't be so hard. After all, he had made no rules about the guessing. She could guess as many names as she wanted. Eventually she would get it right.

The next morning, the door to her office opened and in popped the minor mutant.

"And what do you guess is my name?" he asked.

"Is it Pythagoras?" she queried. "Is it Zeno? Is it Euclid?"

"No, no, and no." He hopped delightedly from one foot to the other.

"Is it Nicomachus? Is it Diophantus? Is it Pappus?"

"Be serious."

"Fibonacci? Newton? Liebniz?"

"Ha."

"Is it Bernoulli or Euler or Lagrange?"

"No, no, and no again. You will have to do better than that." And with that he was gone.

All that day, the woman searched in her books for every name she could find. She asked others around the department for any other names they might know.

When the little man arrived the next morning, she asked, "Is it Gauss? Is it Cauchy? Is it Mobius?"

"No, no, and no," he laughed, hardly able to contain himself.

"Is it Lobachevsky? Dirichlet? Liouville?"

"Not even close."

"How about Weierstrauss? Cayley? Hermite? Cantor? Dedekind? Beltrami?"

"No, no, no, no, no, no."

"What about Lie or Poincaré or Peano or Hurwitz or Hilbert or Cartan?"

"Give me a break."

"Maybe Zermelo, Dickson, or Lebesgue?"

"No, no, and no. Tomorrow is your last chance." And with that, he disappeared out the door.

The young professor was crushed. She didn't know what to do.

"Oh, woe is me," she cried. All that day, she wrung her hands, completely distraught. That evening, as she went to get a tissue from the bathroom to dab her tears, she heard a voice singing from within the Men's Room.

"I am so happy, I could sing, as I shower in the sink.
For she doesn't realize who I am,
And how with this department I link.
She doesn't know that I live in the Lounge,
She doesn't know my game.
And she doesn't know the most important part,
Rumpled Stiltsken is my name."

She immediately went to her father's office.

"Pop," she said, "have you ever heard of someone named Rumpled Stiltsken?"

"Oh sure, everybody knows about Rumpled Stiltsken. One of the most brilliant minds to ever grace this campus."

"Who is he?"

"Who was he is the more appropriate question. Bob Stiltsken was a graduate student here thirty years ago. A real star. But he got hooked on Catalan's Conjecture. Spent all his time trying to prove it. Couldn't bring himself to solve an easier problem and get a Ph.D."

"So what happened?"

"After eight years, they cut his support, and threw him out of the program. But he still hung around. Used to sleep in the Math Lounge. Somehow he had gotten hold of a key. About ten years ago, he disappeared entirely. Nobody knows where he went. But there are rumors of a sighting every now and then."

"And why is he called Rumpled Stiltsken?"

"Well, he always wore the same red sports coat, and calling it rumpled is being generous."

The next morning, the pungent person sprang into her office, and said, "Last chance. What's my name?"

The girl smiled and said, "Is it Veblen, or Noether, or Sierpinski?"

"No, no, and no again."

"Is it Birkhoff, or Lefschetz, Littlewood, or Polya?"

"No, no, nope, and no."

"Maybe Ramanujan or Banach, Cech, or Bloch?"

"No, oh no, oh no, and no."

"Klein, Wiener, Nevanlinna, or Urysohn?"

"Nope, nope, nope de nope."

"Artin or Zariski?"

"Double nope."

"Zygmund or Hopf ?"

"No, no."

"Church or Whitehead?"

"No and again a big no. Looks like you are plum out of luck." He was grinning from ear to ear.

"I guess I don't know," she said pausing for a second. "Unless of course, perhaps, it is Rumpled Stiltsken."

The odiferous oddball froze, stunned for an instant. "How could you,..., how did you...?" he spluttered.

"I guess I keep the proof of Catalan's Conjecture after all," she said.

"Arghhh," screamed the minute miscreant, his face turning as red as his jacket. He stomped his feet and gnashed his teeth, and pulled forcefully on his matted hair. His eyes rolled up in his sockets, and then he stormed out of the office, never to be seen at the University of Chicago again.

Since then, every once in a while, reports filter down from the University of Illinois at Chicago of coffee pots found empty just minutes after they had been full. And at Northwestern, department copies of Stewart's Calculus disappear at an alarming rate.

The young professor went on to a very successful career at Chicago. She and her father wrote some joint papers, on the basis of which her father was promoted to an office of reasonable size. And, although she did drink coffee for the next four years, she switched to herbal tea after receiving tenure. And even then, the theorems kept coming.

NOTES

Notes for
"The S.S. Riemann"

The Riemann Hypothesis has been open since 1859, and it is acknowledged by most mathematicians to be the greatest open problem confronting mathematics today. It was first posed by Bernhard Riemann (1826–1866) when he was investigating the distribution of prime numbers.

A number is prime if it has no integer factors other than itself and 1. The mathematical field of number theory seeks to understand the properties of the integers, with particular interest in the primes. Riemann came up with an analytic formula that gave the number of primes below any given integer n. That formula depended on the zeros of the Riemann zeta function.

Let $\zeta(s) = \Sigma_{n=1}^{\infty} \frac{1}{n^s} = \frac{1}{1^s} + \frac{1}{2^s} + \frac{1}{3^s} + \ldots$.

For a given number s, we simply add up all of the values of $\frac{1}{n^s}$ for $n = 1, 2, \ldots$.

This function does not add up to a finite number for real numbers less than 1. But for real numbers greater than 1, it is well defined; for instance, $\zeta(2) = \pi^2/4$ and $\zeta(4) = \pi^4/90$.

If one allows s to take on complex values of the form $a + bi$ where $i = \sqrt{-1}$, one can extend the function by a method called analytic continuation to get a new function that is defined for all complex values of s, but that restricts to the original function when the real part of s is greater than 1. A zero of the Riemann zeta function is a complex number w such that $\zeta(w) = 0$.

It is well known that $\zeta(s) = 0$ for s equal to a negative even integer $-2, -4, -6, \ldots$. These are called the trivial zeros. The Riemann Hypothesis states that the other zeros—the nontrivial zeros—all lie on the line given by $1/2 + bi$. They are all complex numbers with real part $1/2$. In 1986, the first 1,500,000,001 nontrivial zeros of the Riemann zeta function were shown to have real part $1/2$. But no one has yet been able to show this for all the nontrivial zeros. In the year 2000, the Clay Mathematical Institute announced a $1,000,000 prize for the solution to this problem.

If the Riemann Hypothesis turns out to be true, it gives good bounds on the distribution of primes. If it turns out to be false, the distribution of primes could look very different from what we expect.

In this story, the purported solution is an exceptionally complex proof that is created by a large contingent of mathematicians. It has a structure that is designed to withstand a variety of problems that might crop up at particular points in the proof. If one lemma turns out to be incorrect and collapses, the proof holds up, as there is another path through the structure to that point.

In some sense this type of approach to proving theorems occurs all the time. A mathematician or group of mathematicians may have the general outline of a proof in mind, and then they must fill in each of the steps. They might have ideas for filling in one of the steps, and ultimately three fail but two are valid. But ideally, this part of the process normally occurs when one is working on the proof, not once one is traveling the country talking about it.

Although it is not unheard of to find papers in experimental physics with as many as 50 authors, numbers of authors on that scale have yet to occur in mathematics. Fewer than 0.1% of the papers published so far in mathematics have over five authors.

The fundamental difference is that a single advancement in mathematics is not obtained through the collaboration of a variety of mathematicians, culminating in one paper with a large number of authors. More commonly, there is a conjecture that many would like to solve. Over many years, individuals publish papers that move closer to that goal, creating the tools that are eventually used in the ultimate solution. Such was the case with Fermat's Last Theorem, where in 1994, Andrew Wiles utilized the machinery set in place by generations of mathematicians to solve a problem that had been open for 350 years.

Perhaps, some day in the not-too-distant future, one or more mathematicians will discover the tools to finish off the Riemann Hypothesis. But in the mean time, it is nice to know it is out there, and at least so far, it has resisted every attack.

Notes for "Overcoming Math Anxiety"

First of all, I do believe in math anxiety. This story is not intended to imply math anxiety is a figment of the math education community's collective imagination. It certainly is not. But as far as diseases go, I would rather have it than hoof-in-mouth disease.

After this story first came out, I received an angry email. To paraphrase, it said, "Math anxiety is nothing to laugh at. It is real, and I have experienced it. You are a math professor. You look at a problem and a light bulb pops on in your head. It is obvious how to do everything. You have no idea what it is like to experience math anxiety. But me, I'm not like that. I look at a problem and I start to feel queasy. On math exams, my palms sweat, I feel clammy all over, and I hyperventilate. So stop trivializing the problem."

But in fact, I do know that feeling. I have only been through it once, but it was extremely unpleasant.

When I was in high school, I was naturally proficient at mathematics. I never studied for a math exam. I would open the text while waiting in the hall for a test to begin just to remind myself of the formulas. Then I would go in and ace the exam. To me, the solutions seemed obvious and straightforward.

But when I was in graduate school, I had to take some graduate physics courses to fulfill my mathematics Ph.D. requirements. I took the first semester of quantum physics one fall, and then skipped a year before taking the second semester with a different professor. Everyone else had taken the first semester with this same professor.

The time came for our midterm. When I opened the test, I didn't even recognize the terminology. I suddenly felt nauseous. I flipped to the next page, hoping to see something familiar, and understood even less. I thought I was going to be sick. A cold sweat covered my forehead. I stared at the exam for the full hour, writing almost nothing. I didn't even understand what was being asked. After turning it in, I went home, climbed into bed and pulled the covers over my head.

When the professor returned the exams, I failed, the only one in the class to do so. I remember thinking this was the end of my academic career. I had finally hit the wall. The psychological impact was almost enough to derail my career as a mathematician.

The professor asked to talk to me after class. He was understanding and said that if I did better on the final, he would pass me in the course. I learned more quantum physics in the next month and a half than I had learned in the previous semester and a half of study. I knew every notation that was out there.

The final turned out to be a week-long take-home exam. I spent every waking hour on it and turned in a 70-page manuscript, proving every result in a mathematically rigorous way, with epsilon delta arguments. The professor was stunned. He gave me an A for the course, although I suspect that he didn't do more than skim my test. It would have taken him hours to go through it.

At any rate, that was my one experience with math/physics anxiety. But the memory stuck. And when I have students who tell me they have math anxiety, I am very sympathetic. I know that the feeling is real. I try to give them suggestions that will help to minimize the problem. I tell them to make up practice exams from the problems in the book, and to take them under timed conditions, to prepare themselves for the test environment.

For most people, math anxiety comes from a lack of self confidence. Often, it is the result of a teacher in elementary school or high school who derived pleasure from belittling the students, and who convinced this student that they had no aptitude for math. Whenever the student sees a slightly unusual problem, the solution for which is not immediately obvious, she assumes she doesn't have the talent to solve the problem.

But as it says in the story, math anxiety can be overcome. You just do so many problems that you know you can handle anything. From that comes confidence, and the A.

Notes for
"A Difficult Delivery"

In many ways, proving a new theorem does resemble the process of giving birth. You work for an extended period, say nine months, on the original idea you had. And then suddenly, it all comes together. The final event is exhilarating, and amazing, and often extremely painful. Sometimes a proof can be 95% done when you find a problem with it. Perhaps there is a counterexample to the statement of some little lemma upon which the entire structure of the theorem depends. Suddenly, a year's worth of work hangs in the balance. Fix the lemma by finding a way to reword its statement, so that the counterexample can be avoided, and you can still prove the theorem. But otherwise, the entire theorem goes down in flames. You find yourself working late into the night, skipping meals, forgetting appointments, hoping it will come out all right.

One of the best known examples of this occurred after Andrew Wiles announced his solution to Fermat's Last Theorem in 1994. It was reported in major newspapers around the globe. Wiles instantly became the most famous living mathematician.

However, shortly thereafter, another mathematician pointed out an error in the proof of one of the lemmas that Wiles was using in his proof. Wiles immediately set to work to try to patch the problem.

243

After what must have been an incredibly stressful nine months, he managed, with the aid of one of his ex-graduate students, to fix it.

Creative mathematics differs from many other fields in this respect. For example, in the process of writing a poem, a poet will try various words and phrases, eventually settling on a particular choice that hopefully optimizes the aesthetic beauty of the poem. Exchanging a word here or there does not destroy the entire poem. Its value is still preserved at approximately the same level.

But mathematics is unforgiving. You can produce a 100-page paper containing 35 lemmas and propositions proving that the Teichmüller space is negatively curved. But the Teichmüller space is not negatively curved, and the tiny mistake that you made in one lemma can bring the entire paper to its knees.

On the other hand, the unforgiving nature of mathematics is also a benefit. You are either right or wrong, and no one can take that away from you. Your success in the field does not depend on who likes you, how well you schmooze, or how erudite you look behind a podium. Opinion plays a relatively small role in mathematics, influencing what areas are considered hot. But if you prove a powerful theorem that impacts a variety of mathematical fields, you will be heralded as a genius, even if you wash your car more often than you take a shower.

The exhilaration you feel upon giving birth to a new theorem is truly remarkable. It is your theorem. In all the history of humankind, no one has ever proved this mathematical fact before. You and you alone have brought this wondrous new thing into existence. Unfortunately, that feeling lasts approximately five minutes, and then you get back to work struggling to understand the mathematics that stymies you the rest of the time.

Notes for
"A Proof of God"

Much of this story is built around an incident that occurred when I was a junior member in my department. One day, my chairman came by with an envelope that had been addressed to the department and he informed me that as the most junior faculty member, I would have the honor of responding to the enquiry.

Upon opening the envelope, I found a forty-page handwritten manuscript, together with a cover letter explaining that this was an algorithm for trisecting any angle using just compass and straight-edge.

As a math student, I had learned in algebra that the Greeks had sought exactly this, a means of cutting any angle into three equal parts, using just compass and straightedge. It wasn't until 1836 that French mathematician Pierre Wantzel (1814–1848) proved that no such algorithm could ever exist.

On the other hand, as a young mathematician, I considered the possibility that perhaps, just perhaps, some small oversight had been made by multiple generations of mathematicians and maybe, although extremely unlikely, maybe, this one genius had stumbled upon the fact that it could be done. If I did not even look at it, I might go down in history as the idiot who missed this work of genius. So I dutifully sat down and tried the algorithm on a 60 degree angle. It took me over an hour to wade through the paper and determine the result, but upon finishing, lo and behold, it generated an angle of about 19.6 degrees. So I wrote a letter explaining all this and sent it off to the author, feeling quite happy about my good deed.

A week later, there was a knock at my door. There before me appeared an 80-year old retired dentist from a town about an hour away. And he was angry. Red in the face, he waved his manuscript about and accused me of having misunderstood it, possibly intentionally. I tried to calm him down, but to no avail. After haranguing me for quite a while, he waved his hands one last time and disappeared down the hall, still muttering.

I learned a valuable lesson that day. It's sometimes better not to respond to people who are potentially "out there". Rarely do they appreciate the response, and they will often treat your response as the beginning of an ongoing dialogue.

The other two problems mentioned in the story were also open for a long time. For two centuries, mathematicians and amateurs tried to prove that the parallel postulate followed from the other postulates of Euclidean geometry. It was the discovery in 1829 of hyperbolic geometry by the Russian mathematician Nikolai Ivanovich Lobachevsky (1792–1856) and the Hungarian mathematician Janos Bolyai (1802–1860) that demonstrated that a geometry could satisfy the other postulates without satisfying the parallel postulate.

The third mathematics problem also dates back to the Greeks. Squaring the circle is the question of whether or not we can construct a square with the same area as a given circle using just compass and straightedge. This was not proved impossible until 1882, when it was shown that π is a transcendental number. (It cannot yield 0 when plugged into any polynomial). One corollary of this is that the circle cannot be squared.

The nonmathematical problem mentioned, that of using mathematics to prove the existence, or for that matter nonexistence, of God, is not a realistic endeavor. Barring the discovery of a message from God hidden in the later digits of π, hypothesized in one of Carl

Sagan's books, the question of God's existence is an empirical question, and is therefore not amenable to approach through the logic of mathematical proof.

Notes for "The Red Badge of Courage"

The title of this is borrowed from Stephen Crane's powerful 1895 novel of the civil war. War is hell, and to many students, so is math.

Math exams in particular can be daunting. You can't fake your way through a math exam. If you don't know the material, you cannot write a lot to cover up your lack of knowledge, as sometimes works in the humanities. You are either right or you are wrong and the professor can quickly determine which it is.

There is also the frustration that comes from seeing those students for whom "math is easy" breeze through the exams. And there are certainly students who are more talented than others. But that just means that the level of mathematics that is difficult for them is at a higher level than for others.

Even the greatest mathematicians get stuck. That's what doing research in mathematics is all about—reaching a level where you get stuck. Then you begin puzzling over it and struggling with it, sometimes for months or years at a time until you eventually figure it out or give up. Often, students think that if they can't get a problem in an hour, they are stupid. An hour is nothing.

There was one problem that I worked on for fifteen years. I made various advances but still couldn't crack the problem. Then two other mathematicians, working together, solved it. And although it was disappointing to me, I did figure out a lot of mathematics over those fifteen years, and the techniques were useful for related problems. So I do not feel like that time was wasted.

Notes for "Journey to the Center of Mathematics"

I always loved the 1959 movie, "Journey to the Center of the Earth," with James Mason playing Professor Oliver Lindenbrook, Pat Boone as his nephew Alec, and Gertrude the Duck playing the duck. She did a great job with that role, but the duck was a script writer's add-in. There is no duck in either the original novel or my version of the story.

The conclusion of the story, that there is nothing at the center of mathematics, is in my mind, one of the most interesting ideas in mathematics. You can start with absolutely nothing, and even then, you have something, the set consisting of absolutely nothing. It has no elements, but it is still a set, so it is something. Now you can form a set that has an element, namely the set that has this very set as its only element. Now you have two sets, the original empty set and this new one. Put them together in another set and you now have a set of two elements. Continuing in this way, you can construct the natural numbers, the operations on the natural numbers, and from that, all of mathematics. It doesn't get any better than that.

Notes for "The Integral: A Horror Story"

The original title of this piece was "Stephen King's 'The Integral'".
At the last minute, I changed the title so as not to get sued. But in
writing it, I tried to imagine how Stephen King would write a horror
story with a mathematical theme.

If you are going to write a story mixing math with horror, there
is a good chance that it will involve math anxiety. This is the place
where fear and math overlap.

The image of the bed canopy slowly lowering to smother the sleeping figure is one I stole from a movie called "The Thirteen Ghosts".
I saw it for my sister's birthday party when I was ten. My mother
regretted taking ten twelve-year-old girls and one ten-year-old boy
to see that memorably scary movie. The facts that the image has
stuck with me until now and that for the next ten years, I refused to
ever sleep in a canopied bed speaks to the vividness of the particular
image. Of course, in the original, there was no integral embroidered
on the canopy.

The blades dropping out of the ceiling as the bed spins below
was an attempt to include a version of Buffon's needle problem. In

1733, Buffon asked how often a needle would land touching a line if you dropped it on a ruled sheet of paper with parallel lines separated by exactly the length of the needle. Interestingly enough, the answer turns out to be $\frac{2}{\pi}$. So dropping needles is a potential means of estimating π. The more times you drop the needle, the closer the ratio of hits to total drops should be to $\frac{2}{\pi}$. But it is not a method that I recommend. There are much more accurate means.

In the situation in the story, Craig represents the line, but rather than moving the needle each time, which was mechanically too difficult, I had the bed turn, so the line moves between drops. Also, it was too difficult to depict the needle as a long slender object landing on its long side, so it became a knife with just a pointed end. However, if you ask how often the blade will hit Craig, the answer turns out to be approximately $\frac{2w}{2\pi r}$, where w is Craig's width and r is the horizontal difference between the hole through which the blades drop and Craig's center. Hence, knowing w and r, we could use the frequency of a hit to obtain an approximation to π.

Once Karen and Craig end up in the tank in the floor, they have to worry about the fact that increments of water are being squirted into the tank at regular intervals. Each subsequent increment is of size $1/n$ gallons. So the total amount of water after n squirts is $1 + 1/2 + \cdots + 1/n$. This is a partial sum for the infinite series $1 + 1/2 + 1/3 + \ldots$, which is known as the harmonic series. This is perhaps the most famous infinite series, or at least, it is in the top three. It has the property that although the terms are individually getting smaller, the series itself is diverging. In other words, the sum is not approaching a finite number. No matter how big a container you pick to hold the water, eventually, as the increments continued to squirt in, the water will overflow the container. It doesn't matter if you picked the Pacific Ocean basin, eventually it will overflow. This is why Numskel has chosen this particular series. He wants to maximize the math anxiety that the situation creates. He needs Karen and Craig to believe they will drown.

But what is interesting about this series is the fact that the partial sums grow so slowly. How many times must the nozzle squirt water in order for the water to yield five gallons? 83 times. How many times for 20 gallons? Over 250,000,000 times. How many times for 100 gallons? Over 1.5×10^{43} times. Figuring 5 seconds per squirt, that would be approximately 2.4×10^{36} years—much longer than the expected life of the universe so far.

Karen realizes this, and therefore experiences no anxiety whatsoever. The fact that the harmonic series diverges was first proved by Nicole d'Oresme (1323–1382) but the proof was mislaid for several centuries. Oh well. No harm done.

And then there is the heptadecagon. The placement of the holes in the wall for the shooting arrows corresponds to the vertices of a 17-gon, also known as a heptadecagon. One of the results that helped to establish Gauss's reputation was his proof that you can construct a 17-gon using a compass and straight-edge. He did this in 1796 at the age of 19.

As far as the violence in this story goes, I apologize. I realize that some readers of math humor are not looking to read something with violence like this in it. But it's hard to write horror without it....

Notes for
"The Three Little Pigs"

For those with a lot of mathematical background, the various references in this story should be self-evident and you might want to skip this note. For others, Swine-erton Dyer corresponds to the Birch and Swinnerton–Dyer Conjecture, which is about solutions of elliptic curves and was first posed by the British mathematicians B. Birch and H.P.F. Swinnerton-Dyer in the early 1960's. Pig = Npig refers to the $P = NP$ Conjecture, an open problem in theoretical computer science first formulated in 1971. And the Hog Conjecture refers to the Hodge Conjecture, which relates to algebraic geometry and which was first posed in 1950. All three of these problems are Clay Millennium problems, meaning that you can get \$1,000,000 for solving any one of them—\$3,000,000 for all three.

Notes for "Class Reunion"

There are so many math references in here that trying to explain them all would yield a note longer than the original story. So let's just mention a few.

The entire piece is a conversation between natural log function and cosine function at the function's high school reunion. Actually, it is natural log's monologue. In it we learn that e^x was married to cosine but is no longer. She looks so young, she can't be differentiated from her mother, a reference to the fact that the derivative of e^x is again e^x.

Natural log calls himself a one-to-one kind of guy because natural log is a one-to-one function. Secant leaves step function because she wants some continuity, and of course, a step function is not continuous. But the irony is that she ends up with absolute value, which although continuous, does not have a continuous first derivative. I know, when you go through and explain the jokes, they sound pretty inane.

The logistic growth function is used to model many real-world situations including drug dissipation, blood alcohol content, constrained population growth, and disease spread.

Then, of course, there is the Riemann Zeta function. As in the notes to "The S.S. Riemann," the Riemann Hypothesis posits that the Riemann Zeta function has all its nontrivial zeros occurring at complex numbers of the form $1/2 + bi$. But showing this has proved to be one of the most challenging problems in mathematics. Unlike your typical polynomial, this function does not divulge where its zeros occur.

Then there is arctan who now works on Wall Street in derivatives. Her old boyfriend $\frac{1}{x^2+1}$ is, in fact, her derivative. He is trying to integrate himself back into society, but he's no arctan. In truth, the integral of $\frac{1}{x^2+1}$ is arctan x.

The polynomial $x^2 + 1$ does not factor when we allow only real numbers for coefficients of the factors, but once we allow complex numbers, it can be factored as $(x + i)(x - i)$.

And of course, cosine knows ups and downs. When graphed, it has infinitely many humps. Enough, or maybe too much, said.

Notes for
"Into Thin Air"

The title is borrowed from John Krakauer's book about the deadly storm on Mt. Everest that caught several expeditions unaware. There are a surprising number of parallels between mountain climbing and theorem proving. But that is what the story is about, isn't it? And who could pass up a title like "Into Thin Air" for a story on mathematical research?

At the time I first wrote this story, the Poincaré Conjecture was open, and it did not appear that a solution was near. First posed by Henri Poincaré in 1904, it has stymied some of the best minds in mathematics. Several well-known mathematicians have claimed solutions only to retract them later. It has a statement for each dimension greater than one.

Its two-dimensional version says that a surface which resembles a sphere is in fact a sphere. In what sense? Notice the difference between a sphere (the surface of a ball) and a torus (the surface of a doughnut). On the first, any closed loop can be shrunk to a point without leaving the surface. But you can create a closed loop on the torus that wraps around the hole of the torus, and that loop cannot be shrunk to a point while remaining on the torus.

In two dimensions, the Poincaré Conjecture considers only compact surfaces. A surface is compact if it can be cut up into a finite number of triangles. These triangles need not be flat triangles. Rather, we think of them as being rubber triangles that can be deformed to be flat.

Both the sphere and torus are compact, as we can take finitely many triangles and glue them together along their edges to obtain these surfaces. However, the plane is not compact, as we would need an infinite number of triangles to construct it.

The Poincaré Conjecture in two dimensions then says that a compact surface such that all loops can be shrunk to points on the surface must be a sphere.

The proof of this two-dimensional version has been known for a long time. But the three-dimensional version was open for 100 years. It said that the same result held for the analog of surfaces one dimension up, called 3-manifolds. A 3-manifold locally looks three-dimensional, just as a surface locally looks two-dimensional. The Poincaré Conjecture says that a compact 3-manifold that has the property that every loop can be shrunk to a point must in fact be the 3-sphere, which is the analog of the sphere one dimension up.

In 2004, Grigory Perelman posted several preprints on the Web that purported to prove the Poincaré Conjecture. After several years of work, referees determined the proof was correct. Although Perelman was awarded the Fields Medal, the highest award in mathematics, for his work, he turned it down, stating that recognition by others was irrelevant to him and not the reason he had sought a solution.

The Poincaré Conjecture is also one of the seven Clay Millennium Math Problems, the solution of any of which yields a prize of one million dollars. It is not yet clear if Perelman will accept the prize, once it is determined that he should receive it.

Notes for
"A Deprogrammer's
Tale"

In some ways, mathematics can be as addictive as drugs. I know mathematicians who have forsaken their spouses, their children, and yes, even their students when they are enmeshed in work on a proof. Quite a few divorces have been attributed to the siren call of mathematics. On the other hand, if you are going to be addicted to something, there are far worse choices than mathematics.

This story posits that the addiction is planned by the mathematical community. This also is not entirely ridiculous. As a mathematics teacher, one of my primary goals is to convince my students that mathematics is beautiful, and that their attempts to understand it can be uplifting, satisfying, and even fun. Then, it will no longer be necessary for their subsequent teachers to require them to do mathematics. They will do it of their own accord, because they enjoy it.

But whatever I do to convince others of the beauty of mathematics, I do not interpret those activities as nefarious attempts to sucker others in. Because mathematics truly is beautiful.

Said like a true addict.

Notes for "Research Announcement"

Mathematics is often perceived as one of the loneliest of endeavors. The mathematician sits sequestered in an office, often late at night, scribbling away, working at a computer or staring off into space, lost in thought, while everyone else is home with their families or out on the town with their friends. Often the professor looks wistfully out the window, wishing for the social abilities to have a life.

And in fact, there are mathematicians who fit much of this stereotype, although most of them would argue they don't look that wistfully out the window. They are very happy working late. In fact, most of mathematics is exactly this—sitting in an office and thinking hard, without distractions.

But nowadays, more often than was true previously, mathematics is a collaborative effort. In the last few years, over half of the mathematics papers published have more than one author. Mathematics is becoming a social endeavor.

The most famous single example of the collaborative approach to mathematics was Paul Erdős, the mathematician who wrote a total of over 1500 papers with over 500 co-authors. He was famous for travelling the world with a suitcase, stopping at universities along the way, disseminating ideas and writing papers with other mathematicians. From him came the concept of the Erdős number which measures how many steps you are away from Erdős. If you wrote a paper with Erdős, your Erdős number is 1. If you wrote a paper with someone who has published with Erdős, your Erdős number is 2. You are only two steps away. Amazingly, almost everyone in mathematics who has published a few papers with others has an Erdős number less than infinity. My own Erdős number is 3. That in itself is surprising, given that I am a topologist and Erdős was a number theorist, two entirely different areas of mathematics.

There are currently 8162 people with Erdős number 2. That number continues to grow. It is interesting to think about what will happen to Erdős numbers over time. Although a paper or two may still appear with Erdős as a co-author (he died in 1996), essentially no additional mathematicians will be added to the list of those with Erdős number 1. At some point those Erdős number 1 people will die off, and unavailable to appear as co-authors, no additional number 2 people will be added to the list.

As the years go by, the number of people with non-infinite Erdős numbers will continue to grow, however, at the same time, the least Erdős number held by a living person will also continue to grow. A little off the topic of the story, but interesting to think about nonetheless. . . .

Does the search for collaborators resemble attempts to meet that special someone? In ways, it does. There are famous pairs in mathematics who found one another, and did some of their best work together: Hardy-Littlewood, Eilenberg-MacLane, Atiyah-Singer. Sometimes, one member of a collaboration brings certain abilities and backgrounds and the other brings the needed complementary ones. As mathematics continues to become more specialized, we should expect to see more and more collaboration. It never hurts to have help.

Notes for "Fields Medalist Stripped"

We don't yet have intelligence-enhancing drugs on the order of the ones described in this story. Or at least ones with proven efficacy. But how long will it be until we do?

In some sense, humanity has been using drugs to aid mental gymnastics for centuries. Caffeine is such a drug. Paul Erdős (1913-1996), who was mentioned in the Notes for "Research Announcement" and who published over 1500 papers in his lifetime, acknowledged that in addition to drinking copious amounts of coffee, he also used amphetamines to stay sharp long into the night.

Mathematicians would be drawn to such drugs for the same reasons that athletes are drawn to steroids and other performance-enhancing drugs. To compete at the highest levels and to know or believe that the competition is taking these drugs makes it very hard to resist. If the drugs do no harm, as seems to be the case with reasonable amounts of caffeine, then perhaps this is fine. But if the drugs do harm, what are we willing to sacrifice for knowledge and/or academic glory?

Notes for "Vital Sines"

Ask any mathematician and she will tell you about when she had a theorem on the emergency room table. The worst-case scenario is if the theorem has been announced and someone finds an error. Then, the mathematician just prays she can fix the hole. More often than not, the error is correctable and the statement of the theorem holds up. But there are those cases where there is an actual counterexample to the theorem, and it all goes down in flames. Then you just want to slink away into a hole and hide for a while, a long while....

Notes for "Rumpled Stiltsken"

This story is a mathematical take on a classic fairytale, with one fundamental change derived from the quote:

"A mathematician is a device for turning coffee into theorems." —Paul Erdős

As mentioned in the previous notes, Paul Erdős led a life entirely devoted to mathematics. He never married, or had a serious relationship with any woman other than his mother. He traveled the world carrying just a suitcase, announcing on arrival at his next stop at whatever university, "My mind is open." This book is dedicated to him.